THE RUNAGATE COURAGE

THE RUNAGATE

*Spite Simplex or
the detailed and wondrously
strange life history of the
archfraud and runagate Courage,
how she first was the
wife of a captain of horse, afterwards
the wife of a captain of infantry,
further the wife of a lieutenant,
presently the wife of a sutler,
the wife of a musketeer,
and finally the wife of a gypsy.
Expertly carried out and excellently
described and just as entertaining,
agreeable, and profitable to contemplate
as Simplicissimus himself.
All of it dictated by the person
of Courage herself
for the displeasure and disgust of
the well-known Simplicissimus
directly to the author who this time
calls himself Philarchus Grossus
of Trommenheim at Griffsberg etc.
Printed in Utopia by Felix Stratiot.*

COURAGE

By
HANS JACOB CHRISTOFFEL VON GRIMMELSHAUSEN

Translated by
ROBERT L. HILLER AND JOHN C. OSBORNE

UNIVERSITY OF NEBRASKA PRESS · LINCOLN

Copyright © 1965 by the University of Nebraska Press
All rights reserved
Library of Congress Catalog card number: 64–19584

Parts IV and V of the Introduction originally appeared in
somewhat different form in the *Germanic Review*.

Manufactured in the United States of America

Preface

The development of the domestic and psychological novel from Richardson in the eighteenth century, through Flaubert, George Eliot, Henry James, Dostoevsky, Tolstoy, and others in the nineteenth century, down to Proust in the twentieth century, constitutes one of the most marvellous chapters in the history of western culture. To match it one would have to recall, say, the efflorescence of painting in Renaissance Italy, or of music in eighteenth and nineteenth century Germany. It is hardly surprising, then, that the word *novel* should by now seem to apply only to prose fiction of this era and this type, or that other prose fiction should often be considered more primitive and less important.

It is not surprising but it is absurd. For "other prose fiction" has its own list of glories: *The Arabian Nights* and *The Decameron, Don Quixote* and *Tom Jones* and *Pickwick Papers* and *The Good Soldier Schweyk, Robinson Crusoe* and *Michael Kohlhaas*, the *Pilgrim's Progress* and *The Castle*. And if it is possible, when immersed in the splendors of Dostoevsky or James, to feel that, compared with these, other kinds of fiction must be trivial, it is possible, when immersed in Cervantes or Kafka, Grimm or Andersen, to feel that the more domestic form of fiction is entirely uncalled for. I am one of those who have often felt this, though I am far from wishing to give such feelings any lasting status. I mention them only to prove the possibility of a prejudice directly opposite to the current one. A prejudice: for when I hear that a book is "not a novel in the usual sense," but is a "romance," a "tale," or a "fable," I am already pleased. If, for use on the proverbial desert island, I were made to choose between a library of "tales" and a library of "novels"—no titles or authors indicated—I'm afraid I would choose the library of tales.

Grimmelshausen is one author I would pray might be included. Why is he not better known among us? One obvious reason is that English translations have not been available, but that this is by no means the only reason is indicated in some remarks made by the very translator of the *Simplicissimus*, A. T. S. Goodrick, in his introduction to the Bison Book edition, to the effect that the book is of less artistic than historical interest. That translation was first published in 1912, and one can only hope that since then some readers have grown a little more sympathetic to the "tale" as distinct from the "novel." Hasek and Kafka have had readers; and such a book as Saul Bellow's *Augie March* would indicate that picaresque storytelling is no un-American activity. Readers of Hasek, Kafka, and Bellow will not be misled by the abundance of incident in their books into the notion that the main purpose of such writing is documentary; just as they will not be misled by the lightness of texture into the notion that these authors do not mean business.

Readers of "novels," on the other hand, have developed a hostility toward abundant incident, toward plot, which they will have to un-learn before they can enjoy tales. For, in tales, plot is not an external and uncalled-for "apparatus" it is the soul of the fiction (as Aristotle said it was of tragedy). As for the flippant tone of the picaresque tradition, what is it but the tone of comedy—the necessary tone for a certain, perfectly serious critique of life? A historian of the novel can make of his history book a kind of success story by representing a novel by Jane Austen as a step forward from the mere "storytelling" of Daniel Defoe, yet what is this but mere cunning in selection? Is a Jane Austen "novel" better than Dickens' "tale" of the *Pickwick Papers*, which was written later? Richardson and Fielding wrote at the same time. The "novel" was to develop out of Richardson's work, not Fielding's, but does that make him a better writer? He was a worse writer.... And so on. Between us and the storytellers a number of pseudo-critical or pseudo-historical barriers have been erected. Perhaps my remarks will help to break them down. Certainly this book will. In the Hiller-Osborne translation, Grimmelshausen is utterly winning.

Who is not won by the story itself is not likely to be won by commentary on it, and yet I cannot refrain from praising Messrs. Hiller and Osborne for their introduction, and particularly for freeing this type of picaresque literature from the implied charge that it is *mere* narrative or *mere* realism. I am referring to pages 18–20 where they make it clear that, in the seventeenth century, realism and symbolism, straight narrative and allegory, were not mutually exclusive propositions. Picaresque literature has been underrated hitherto because of a refusal to see the "non-realistic" elements in it. It has come to seem trivial because of a refusal to see its non-trivial elements. The triviality of commentators has attached itself to the object of their commentary.

One does not read *The Runagate Courage* merely as a source of Brecht's *Mother Courage*. That would be grossly unfair to the great artist that Grimmelshausen was in his own right. Whether the modern reader can come to *The Runagate Courage* except *by way of* Brecht's play is another question, Brecht being a known quantity, Grimmelshausen an unknown one. Who can say how much that is going to affect the image which Grimmelshausen will evoke in our minds? Historians of the narrower school will be shocked at the thought of such "distortion," yet historians with a little more history will know that this sort of thing happens all the time, for the past is never seen directly but always as reflected in mirrors of the present. . . .

Messrs. Hiller and Osborne have good things to say about Brecht too (pages 21–27). I am not sure that the Grimmelshausen "inspired" as much of Brecht's *Mother Courage* as they imply, but certainly there is a degree of such inspiration, and, equally certainly, the influence worked out dialectically: Brecht begins by wishing to "say the opposite" but ends by saying something that is, to a certain extent, the same. Messrs. Hiller and Osborne enrich our understanding of Brecht by pointing this out, and they enrich it even more in a passage I have just mentioned in another connection:

> Underlying the tale of the adventuress and courtesan are three typically Baroque themes: The first deals with the dangers of disturbing the harmonies of nature; the second argues the proposition *mulier non homo;* the third demonstrates the vanity of the finite world. Viewing the book as a whole, the heroine's life history constitutes an allegory on the nature of courage . . . (p. 18).

This passage not only gives us more than a hint that we might read Brecht too with an eye to moral dialectics. It prompts the question whether Mother Courage does not treat these very Baroque themes, albeit in non-seventeenth-century terms. For the playwright did not share the usual modern contempt for the picaresque. He wished to restore plot to a place of honor, and he was interested in combining multiplicity of incident with an over-arching structure that was both thematic and schematic.

Eric Bentley

Berlin, December, 1964

Contents

List of Engravings

By Jacques Callot

Introduction

The points of likeness between the seventeenth century and our own are numerous and impressive: both shuddered under the impact of devastating wars which wiped out whole cities and took an unprecedented toll of human life; both saw massive displacements of people all over Europe and the emergence of new centers of political power; during both, a tremendous spate of inventions and scientific discoveries occurred within a brief span of time, abruptly imposing a new view of the universe and of man himself—old beliefs and concepts had to be either discarded willy-nilly or incorporated indiscriminately into the life structure of an unfamiliar, exciting, and terrifying world. Given these parallels, it is not surprising that the work of the seventeenth-century German novelist Hans Jacob Christoffel von Grimmelshausen has, in Eric Bentley's phrase, "a terrible relevance" for us today.

I

The Runagate Courage (*Die Landstörtzerin Courasche*) is one of three novels which form the major part of what are now generally known as the Simplician writings, so called because they are derived from or tenuously connected with *The Adventurous Simplicissimus* (*Der Abentheurliche Simplicissimus*) and were written by its author.[1] Although today *Simplicissimus* is considered to be the most outstanding German novel of the seventeenth century, it was not a critical success when it first appeared. One learned critic, Christian Weise, described its

1. The full titles of the first editions of *Simplicissimus* and of the three Simplician novels are given in Appendix A. English translations of *Simplicissimus* are available in paperback editions published by the University of Nebraska Press (Bison Book 134), by Ungar, and by the Liberal Arts Press.

narrator as "a tedious teller of old and useless tales," and another,
Johannes Rist, relegated the novel itself to the category of "useless
junk." [2] But *Simplicissimus* more than made up for its critical failure by
its commercial success. In the four years following its first appearance,
presumably at the Frankfurt spring book fair of 1668, it went through
five editions, at least two of which went into a second printing.
Perhaps the best indication of its popularity is the number of other
literary works which attempted to capitalize on its success. By 1675
fifteen different books had been published which treated characters
from *Simplicissimus*, or were supposed to be written by Simplicissimus
or one of the Simplician characters, or mentioned the words "Simplicissimus" or "Simplician" prominently in the title; and by 1700 more
than thirty such works had appeared.

The Adventurous Simplicissimus is a picaresque narrative purporting
to be the autobiography of the title character. *The Runagate Courage*—
the first work to be derived from it—takes as its point of departure an
incident related in the sixth chapter of the fifth book:

> There was in Sauerbrunnen a beautiful lady who claimed to be nobility, but
> to my mind was more *mobilis* than *nobilis*; this mantrap, because she seemed
> rather sleek of appearance, I courted most diligently, and soon gained not
> only entrance to her house but also all the pleasures which I might have
> wished and desired; but I straightway felt disgusted at her wantonness, and
> therefore pondered how I might rid myself of her in good manner, for it
> seemed to me that she was more inclined to milk my purse than to get me for
> a husband; on top of that she pursued me everywhere with alluring, fiery
> glances and other signs of her burning affection so that I felt ashamed for her
> sake as well as for my own.

2. Information on the critical reception of *Simplicissimus* and its imitators
(discussed below) will be found in Gisela Herbst, *Die Entwicklung des Grimmels-
hausenbildes in der wissenschaftlichen Literatur* (Bonn: H. Bouvier u. Co. Verlag,
1957), pp. 10, 12, 137–144; details of its printing history in Manfred Koschlig,
*Grimmelshausen und seine Verleger. Untersuchungen über die Chronologie seiner
Schriften und den Echtheitscharakter der frühen Ausgaben*, Berlin dissertation (Weimar,
1939), pp. 68–205.

The "beautiful lady," whose name is nowhere given, is Courage. Enraged that Simplicissimus should make public her shame and his own, she decides to "spite Simplex" by telling her own life story and showing him "what kind of honorable minx he was dealing with so that he may know of what he bragged and may perhaps wish that he had kept silent" (Chapter 1). In the second of the Simplician novels, *The Strange Hopalong* (*Der seltzame Springinsfeld*), the young student to whom Courage dictated her story relates how he happened to meet her and how she rewarded him for his labors in her behalf. The title character, the quondam musketeer Hopalong, plays a prominent role in both *Simplicissimus* and *The Runagate Courage*.[3]

It is not known precisely when *Courage* first appeared, for none of its three editions bears a date of publication. It was announced by Wolf Eberhard Felszecker, who also published *Simplicissimus*, in the catalogs of the Frankfurt and Leipzig spring book fairs in 1670, and it is known to have been on sale at the Frankfurt autumn book fair in September of that year. A second edition soon followed, and because it was revised in much the same way as the pirated third edition of *Simplicissimus* some scholars hold that it is likewise a piracy, perhaps by the same Georg Muller of Frankfurt who is believed responsible for the pirated *Simplicissimus*. The pirated third edition of *Courage*, which presumably appeared in the early 1670's, seems to have been based on the first edition.

The real name of the author of *Simplicissimus, Courage,* and the other Simplician novels was not known until well into the nineteenth century. The author himself was in no small measure responsible for this situation, for he delighted in attributing his works to persons with fanciful names, all of which were anagrams of one another. *Simplicissimus* allegedly was composed by one German Schleifheim von Sulsfort, and Philarchus Grossus von Trommenheim is listed as the author of both *Courage* and *Hopalong.* The first part of *The Magic Bird's Nest* (*Das wunderbarliche Vogel-nest*) is attributed to Michael Rechulin von

3. See Appendix B for a translation of the chapters which treat of Courage.

Sehmsdorf, but the second part has in place of an author's name a string of initials—A C EEE FF G HH II LL MM NN OO RR SSS T UU— the letters from which, more or less, the preceding names are composed. The authors of other Simplician writings bear yet other anagrammatic names: Simon Lengfrisch von Hartenfels, Erich Steinfels von Grufensholm, and Israel Fromschmidt von Hugenfelsz.[4]

That all these works were written by one man was taken for granted: The anagrammatic names indicated as much, and furthermore all of them were included in the edition of the collected Simplician works which Felszecker published in 1683–1684, 1685–1699, and 1713. However, both contemporaries and eighteenth-century scholars and lexicographers believed that their author's real name was none of those already mentioned, but was rather Samuel Greifenson vom Hirschfeld, whose biblical novel *Des Vortrefflich Keuschen Josephs Lebensbeschreibung* was also included in the collected works. Grimmelshausen himself, characteristically, was responsible for this mistake. In the so-called "*Beschluss*," which was included in the second, six-book edition of *Simplicissimus* and in the separate printing of the sixth book, a commentator who identified himself only as H. I. C. V. G., P. zu Cernheim noted: "This *Simplicissimus* is a work by Samuel Greifenson vom Hirschfeld, for I found it after his death among his papers, and especially as he himself refers in this work to the *Keuscher Joseph*, which he wrote, and refers in his *Satyrischer Pilgram* to his *Simplicissimus*, part of which he wrote in his youth when he was still a musketeer; for what reason he changed his name by rearranging its letters and instead of it used German Schleifheim von Sulsfort is not known to me."

In 1838 it was finally established that the author of *Simplicissimus, Courage,* and the other Simplician writings was not Greifenson but the H. I. C. V. G., P. zu Cernheim of the "*Beschluss*": Hans Jacob Christoffel von Grimmelshausen, Praetor (chief magistrate) at Renchen, the avowed author of *Simplicianischer Zwyköpffiger Ratio Status* and of two courtly novels also included in the "collected works," *Dietwalts und Amelinden anmuthige Liebs- und Leidsbeschreibung* and *Des Durchleuchtigen*

4. A list of the works in question appears in Appendix A.

Printzen Proximi und seiner ohnvergleichlichen Lympidae Liebs-Geschicht-Erzehlung.[5] In all fairness to Grimmelshausen, it must be noted that while he misled his readers and generations of scholars in the "*Beschluss,*" he did permit himself to be identified as the author of *Simplicissimus* and *Courage* in two poems which were printed with *Dietwald und Amelind* and were perhaps intended to stimulate interest in *Courage.*[6] In the second strophe of the first poem the poet says of Grimmelshausen:

> He may write of what he will, of matters great or small,
> In earnest or in jest, or tales which please us all,
> Of Simplicissimo, his mother and his dad,
> Of old Courage's life, of man and lass and lad.

The second poem refers to both Courage and Hopalong:

> I, with most ardent desire,
> Await what Courage will tell:
> Whether she still leads an evil life
> And cares naught for Heav'n nor Hell,
> How Hopalong now fares,
> And whether he's mended his ways,
> Or whether, as before,
> He still with scoundrels strays.

5. See Appendix A for the full titles of these two works.
6. Herbst (above, note 2), p. 8, reprints both poems. The original German is as follows:

> Er schreibe was Er woll, von schlecht, von hohen Sachen,
> Von Schimpf, von Ernst, von Schwäncken die zu lachen machen
> > von Simplicissimo, der meuder and dem Knan
> > von der Courage alt, von Weiber oder Man.
> > Mit höchst gierigem Verlangen
> > wart ich, was Courage sagt,
> > Ob sie noch führt schlimmes Leben
> > und nach Frömmigkeit nichts fragt,
> > Wie sich Springinsfeld anläszt,
> > ob er sei ein Frommer worden,
> > Oder sich noch wie zuvor aufhält
> > in dem schlimmen Orden.

II

Up until Grimmelshausen was identified as the author of *Simplicissimus*, and even for some time afterward, it was generally assumed
that the book was almost completely autobiographical. According to
his own account, Simplicissimus is a foundling of noble birth, who
comes into the world on June 22, 1622, the date of the battle of Höchst
during the Thirty Years' War (1618–1648). While still a small child he
is forced to flee into the forest when his foster parents' home is attacked
by marauding soldiers. For two years he lives in innocence and piety
with an anchorite, who in reality is his natural father. When the
anchorite dies, the boy wanders to the Protestant fortress of Hanau.
In the garrison there he is dressed in fool's clothes because he is simple
and naive, but he soon learns the evil ways of the world and becomes
an accomplished dissembler. While at play outside the fortress walls he
is seized by an Imperialist raiding party, and after many hardships and
adventures he reaches Westphalia, where his talent for taking booty
makes him renowned as "the huntsman of Soest." Now his only
thoughts are of material gain. For a time he lives in princely fashion in
Cologne, but his fortunes change and he flees to Paris. After serving as
apprentice to a quacksalver he becomes a famous opera singer and
much sought-after gallant. But this life of ease and luxury is soon over,
and he returns to Germany ailing and impoverished. He again joins
the army, this time as a musketeer, then becomes the companion of
highwaymen, and finally is appointed commander of a company of
soldiers. When his best friend is wounded Simplicissimus accompanies
him to a watering place (Sauerbrunnen), where the friend dies.
Simplicissimus then settled down as a farmer, but this is clearly not the
life for him and he again sets out on adventures which take him to
Moscow, whence he returns to Germany by way of Egypt, Italy, and
Switzerland. Home once more, he realizes the vanity of his quest for
worldly fame and fortune. Like his father before him, he withdraws
from the world to end his days as an anchorite.

A century of painstaking research has proved that the life of Grimmelshausen was quite different from that of his hero. So far as can be ascertained, Hans Jacob Christoffel von Grimmelshausen was born in or near Gelnhausen, a village in the Spessart, in either 1621 or 1622. While he was yet a child his father died and his mother remarried and moved away, leaving him in the care of his paternal grandparents, who were well-to-do but by no means wealthy. At the age of six or seven Grimmelshausen began attending the Lutheran school at Gelnhausen, receiving instruction in reading, writing, arithmetic, Latin, and the tenets of the Augsburg Confession. His formal schooling ended in September, 1634, when Protestant Gelnhausen was taken and plundered by Catholic Imperial troops. Apparently his grandparents took him to the Protestant fortress of Hanau in early December, but in January while he was playing outside the fortifications the lad was seized by an Imperial raiding party. A month or so later he was captured by anti-Imperialist Hessian troops and taken to Cassel. In the summer of 1636 he apparently was present at the second siege of Magdeburg and at the battle of Wittstock. During the winter of 1636–1637 he is presumed to have been at the Imperial winter quarters in Soest, where he joined a regiment of dragoons under the command of the Imperial field marshal, Count Götz, and participated in the campaigns of 1637 and 1638 along the Upper Rhine. During the spring of 1638 Götz' army set out to succor the garrison at Breisach, then under siege by Protestant forces. En route Götz took Offenburg, a fortified city on the Kinzig River not far from the Rhine, but the attempt to relieve Breisach failed. After wintering with the army in Suabia, Grimmelshausen returned to Offenburg and enlisted as a musketeer in the regiment of Lieutenant Colonel Hans Reinhard von Schauenburg. In 1640 he was assigned as scribe to the regimental secretary and served in this capacity until 1647; he was then transferred to another Imperial fortress, Wasserburg, and served as regimental secretary under von Schauenburg's brother-in-law, Colonel Johann Burkard von Elter, until the end of the war.

Grimmelshausen's connection with the von Schauenburgs did not end with the war. After his return to Offenburg and his marriage on August 30, 1649, to an officer's daughter, Katharina Henninger, he was appointed steward (*Schaffner*) of the hereditary von Schauenburg domains in and around Gaisbach, a village in the Rench valley near Oberkirch. Grimmelshausen began his stewardship as the servant of three masters, Hans Reinhard, his former commanding officer, and two other von Schauenburgs, Carl Bernhard and Claus. He fell out of favor with Claus, but continued to serve the other two until 1655, when he gave up Carl's stewardship, presumably because his work for Hans Reinhard was almost more than he could manage. His duties included keeping all accounts, attending to minor legal matters concerning financial transactions, and collecting the fees, duties, and taxes due the lords of the estate. He was, in addition, Hans Reinhard's private secretary and in his behalf undertook inspections of the widely scattered von Schauenburg properties. For all these services he apparently was paid the modest sum of about thirty sovereigns a year.

In 1653 Grimmelshausen succeeded in acquiring a rundown piece of property in Gaisbach, the "Spitalbühne"—it appears in his works as "Hybspinthal"—where the foreword to *Satyrischer Pilgram* and the Dedication to *Dietwald un Amelind* allegedly were composed. He built two houses on the Spitalbühne, occupying one of them, and at the same time continued to maintain a residence in Gaisbach at Hans Reinhard's steward's house. In 1657 he acquired a permanent home in Gaisbach by trading his unoccupied house on the Spitalbühne for the steward's house belonging to Phillip Hannibal von Schauenburg, son and heir of the now deceased Claus. As part of the bargain, Grimmelshausen received the privilege of maintaining a public house in the large room on the ground floor.

As was customary at the time, he had speculated with the properties and income of the family he served, and his debts to them gradually increased until at last, on September 7, 1660, Grimmelshausen relinquished his post as steward, possibly at Hans Reinhard's request. Until 1662 he seems to have supported himself and his growing family by plying the innkeeper's trade "at the sign of the Silver Star"; then he was entrusted with a stewardship by a wealthy Strassburg doctor, Johann Küffer the Younger, who had acquired some property near Gaisbach and was setting himself up as a country squire. This time too his stewardship ended with hard feelings, and the year 1666 saw him once more employed as innkeeper. Now, however, in order to earn more money for his ever increasing family (all told he had ten children), Grimmelshausen began to spend much of his time in the second-floor study of the steward's house, composing some of the works which were to make him famous.

On March 16, 1667, he was appointed chief magistrate (*Schultheiss*) of Renchen, a village of about seven hundred people, seat of one of the six courts under the jurisdiction of the Oberkirch district, one of eleven districts making up the secular possessions of the bishopric of Strassburg. As well as presiding over the court, the chief magistrate was charged with collecting taxes, carrying out the orders of the community's governor (*Obervogt*), guarding public funds set aside for Renchen's orphans and wards, and ensuring public safety and obedience to the laws and ordinances. Grimmelshausen continued to serve in this post until his death on August 16, 1676.

III

Whereas Simplicissimus performed feats of daring during the Thirty Years' War, achieving some fame as a soldier and adventurer, his creator spent eight or nine of his thirteen army years as a garrison soldier, far from the heat of battle. The war nonetheless was the most important experience in Grimmelshausen's life, and since it forms the background for *Simplicissimus*, *Courage*, and the other Simplician novels, a brief sketch of its history may help to place Courage's adventures and Grimmelshausen's own wartime activities in their proper context.[7]

The war began in 1618 when the Bohemian Protestants rebelled against Matthias, Emperor of Austria and King of Bohemia, because they feared that his heir apparent, Archduke Ferdinand of Styria, would institute policies of religious repression in their land as he already had done in Styria. Bohemia was politically important because its king automatically became an elector of the Holy Roman Empire and thus had a voice in the affairs of Germany. In 1619, after Matthias' death and the archduke's accession to the throne of Austria as Emperor Ferdinand II, the electors met and dutifully appointed him King of Bohemia. Several days earlier, however, the Bohemian rebels had offered their crown to the Elector Palatine, Frederick, who was the nominal head of the Protestant Union in Germany and had helped subsidize the mercenary army of Count Ernest von Mansfeld in a campaign to aid the Bohemian Protestants. When Frederick accepted the crown, Duke Maximilian of Bavaria, the most powerful prince in the Catholic League in Germany, secretly agreed to help Ferdinand in Bohemia if Ferdinand would see to it that Frederick was deposed from his electorship and Maximilian made an Imperial prince-elector in his place.

Ferdinand needed Maximilian's assistance, for during the first two years of the war it appeared that the empire of the Austrian Habsburgs was about to collapse. Aided by Mansfeld's mercenaries, the Bohemian Protestants had gained control of nearly all their own country and were preparing to attack Austria itself; in the duchies of Lusatia and Silesia and in the margravate of Moravia, the Protestants had rebelled and driven out their Habsburg masters; and in still another Habsburg kingdom, Hungary, an invasion by Bethlen Gabor, the Calvinist Prince of Transylvania, had touched off a Protestant revolt.

The tide began to turn in 1620 when Maximilian's army, led by

7. C. V. Wedgewood, *The Thirty Years War* (New Haven: Yale University Press, 1939) was the primary source for the following summary and for the historical notes in the text.

Marshal Tilly, joined forces with the Imperial army under Comte de Bucquoy and invaded Bohemia, defeating the Bohemian Protestants and ending the reign of their "Winter King," Frederick, at the battle of White Hill. Courage's story has its beginning during this campaign when Prachatitz falls to Bucquoy, and Courage (whose nurse has disguised her as a boy to protect her from the soldiery) is impressed into service as valet-de-chambre to a captain of horse (Chapter 2). In 1621 Bucquoy's army reconquered Moravia, as Courage relates (Chapters 3 and 4), and probably would have driven the Protestants completely out of Hungary too had not Bucquoy been killed in battle.

While Maximilian and Bucquoy were taking Bohemia, most of the Palatinate, Frederick's rightful territory, was occupied by a part of the Spanish Habsburg army, which was in Flanders awaiting an opportunity to subjugate the Protestant United Provinces of the Netherlands. Once Bohemia had been reconquered, Tilly led Maximilian's army into the Palatinate to join the Spanish forces under Cordoba, and in May of 1622 the Catholic allies defeated a Protestant army at Wimpfen, in a battle which Courage describes as "pleasant, almost merry" (Chapter 7). Six weeks later Tilly and Cordoba defeated the newly raised Protestant army of Prince Christian of Brunswick in the battle of Höchst (Chapter 8). Meanwhile the United Provinces had come to Frederick's aid, subsidizing his efforts to regain the Palatinate, and subsequently were invaded by the main body of the Spanish army, which had remained in Flanders. During the next year, 1623, Tilly's Bavarian army chased the Protestant forces clear to the Dutch border, and the first phase of the war ended with Maximilian in possession of Frederick's electoral vote and almost all the Rhineland and the Palatinate under Imperial control.

Recognizing the threat this posed to France, Louis XIII's chief minister of state, Cardinal Richelieu, formed an alliance with the United Provinces, England, Sweden, and Denmark. France and her allies hoped to cut the supply lines between Spain and her army in Flanders, and in 1625 occupied the Val Telline as well as sending armies to Alsace and Lorraine, but the plan failed when the Spanish took the key fortress of Breda. In 1626 an army raised by Christian IV of Denmark to check Imperial advances in the north was soundly defeated by the combined forces of Marshal Tilly and Wallenstein, general of the Austrian Imperial army, at Lutter, a battle in which Courage and her horse "received hard blows . . . but got off with nothing more than bumps and bruises" (Chapter 11). The next year, while she was playing the grand lady of a Danish count (Chapter 13), Wallenstein occupied neutral Brandenburg, pursued Christian's forces down the Elbe, and then occupied Schleswig, Holstein, Jutland, and Mecklenburg.

The years 1628 and 1630 proved pivotal in the history of the Thirty Years' War and no less so in the life of Courage, who again attaches herself to the Imperial army, no longer to be an officer's lady but a sutler woman and the mistress of a common soldier (Chapters 14–22). In 1628 the Duke of Mantua died, leaving his duchy to a distant relative who was a French subject. Since the Habsburgs dared not permit the French to control the fortress of Mantua and that of Casale, in neighboring Montserrat, Emperor Ferdinand sequestered the duchy. When Richelieu sent a force to relieve the garrison at Casale, Imperial troops from northern Germany—and Courage with them (Chapters 14–15)— marched to Italy and laid siege to the two strongholds (Chapters 16–21). Wallenstein's advance in the north was checked when he was unable to take Stralsund on the Baltic, but Mantua finally capitulated to the Imperial army in 1630, and France again withdrew from the war. After her return to Austria with the Imperial army, Courage too decides to sit out the rest of the fighting and retires to Passau (Chapters 22–23).

Now that the Habsburgs held most of the strategic fortresses they needed, their luck seemed to run out. Wallenstein, who had become too powerful to please the Imperial princes, was relieved of his command in 1630; and when Gustavus Adolphus, Sweden's king, invaded Germany at the head of a Protestant army in July of that year, there was no one to face him but Marshal Tilly, now old and infirm.

After vanquishing Tilly at Breitenfeld, near Leipzig, the invaders occupied the Rhineland. By 1632 they had moved into Bavaria, and in view of the mounting threat to his empire, Ferdinand had no choice but to reinstate Wallenstein. Instead of advancing and engaging Gustavus Adolphus, Wallenstein occupied Prague—to which city Courage flees when she leaves Passau (Chapter 23)—then suddenly struck out for Saxony, endangering his foe's northern base of operations. Gustavus Adolphus countered by moving his forces northward, and the two armies clashed at Lützen on November 16, 1632. Aided by Bernhard of Saxe-Weimar, Gustavus Adolphus carried the day but was mortally wounded.

Wallenstein survived his greatest adversary by only two years, and the possibility of peace or of Imperialist victory died with him. Germany's agony was to be prolonged for fourteen more years, during which she was an arena for French, Spanish, Swedish, and Austrian armies. She continued to suffer irreparable losses of men and wealth; her towns were destroyed and her trade disrupted; her peasantry was reduced to living in the most abject and barbarous conditions; and indeed living conditions sharply retrogressed in every class of society.

For a brief time it appeared that the Imperial forces might regain the upper hand in Germany. In 1634 an army led by King Ferdinand of Hungary, heir apparent to the Austrian throne, took Regensburg and laid siege to the Swedish fortress of Nördlingen. Reinforced by Spanish troops, Ferdinand inflicted a serious defeat on the Protestant armies of Marshal Horn and Bernhard of Saxe-Weimar when they came to relieve the garrison. Courage, who had lost yet another husband in this battle (Chapter 23), was with the Imperial forces when they followed up their victory by sweeping northward into Württemberg, Hesse, and Westphalia. At about this time, young Grimmelshausen found refuge in the Protestant fortress at Hanau.

The Imperial victories brought France back into the war; and from this time on it became increasingly a struggle between two powerful dynasties, the Bourbons of France and the Habsburgs of Austria and

Spain. By 1637, when Grimmelshausen joined the Imperial army, the Protestants again were on the offensive. Bernhard of Saxe-Weimar defeated the Imperial troops at Rheinfelden in the spring of 1638 and then besieged Breisach. Grimmelshausen, as has been noted, took part in the futile campaign to relieve this vital stronghold, which capitulated in December. Of the major fortresses along the Rhine, only Offenburg under the command of Grimmelshausen's future patron, Colonel von Schauenburg, remained in Imperial hands until the signing of the Peace of Westphalia.

In 1642 Lennart Torstenson, the Swedish commander in chief, won the second battle of Breitenfeld and menaced the hereditary states of the Austrian emperor. In 1643 a French army led by the Duc d'Enghien defeated the Spanish Imperial troops at Rocroi near the Flemish border, and Spain's hold on the Netherlands was finally weakened. In 1645, the year in which Courage's last husband "turned up dead . . . at the battle of Herbsthausen" (Chapter 26), Swedish troops under Torstenson and Königsmark all but annihilated an Imperial army at Magedeburg. Torstenson then conquered Moravia, invaded Bohemia, and was less than a hundred miles from Vienna when an outbreak of the plague forced him to withdraw; meanwhile, the French under Marshal Turenne marched to the Danube and joined Königsmark's army. At this point Courage casts in her lot with the gypsies with whom she is to spend the rest of her life (Chapter 27). In the fall of 1646, after serving with Königsmark, the gypsy band is attached to the Swedish main army (Chapter 28). Two years later, with Bavaria occupied by Turenne, Prague besieged by Königsmark, and the Spanish army wiped out by the Duc d'Enghien, the signing of the Treaty of Westphalia brought the Thirty Years' War to a close.

Since Grimmelshausen could have had no firsthand knowledge of the military events to which Courage refers—indeed, he was no more than a babe in arms when she was fighting in the battle of Höchst—it is not surprising that he is guilty of historical inaccuracies. Prachatitz, for example, had changed hands twice before its conquest in 1620, described by Courage in Chapter 2. Budweis was not taken by Maximilian's army alone, as Courage states in the same chapter, but by the combined armies of Maximilian and Bucquoy; only after the victory did the armies split up. And Pilsen was not taken at all, and no "pitiable slaughter and hangings" occurred there (Chapter 3). An even more glaring error is Courage's assertion that "Cordoba and von Anhalt once more defeated the Prince of Brunswick and Mansfeld at Fleurus" (Chapter 8), for in fact Brunswick and Mansfeld routed the outnumbered Imperial troops in that engagement. These inaccuracies may be attributed to Grimmelshausen's historical source, Wassenberg's *Erneuerter Teutscher Florus*, which he copies, often verbatim.[8]

Other errors in fact and historical chronology no doubt are due to the haste with which Grimmelshausen evidently wrote *Courage*. The references to Bethlen Gabor's siege of Pressburg in Chapter 4 and to Mansfeld's withdrawal from Weidhausen in Chapter 6 indicate that Grimmelshausen either did not know or did not care about the chronology of these events. Bethlen gave up the siege of Pressburg on September 5, 1621, and Mansfeld retired from his fortified position at Weidhausen on October 10 of the same year. Thus the adventures which Courage relates in Chapters 5 and 6, although they seem to occupy a longer period of time, must have taken place in slightly more than one month.

By contrast, Grimmelshausen's picture of general conditions during the war appears to be quite accurate, perhaps because after the first years of the struggle there was no appreciable change in the composition of armies, in the crudeness and brutality of everyday military life, and in the manner which the troops harassed and exploited the townsman and the peasant.

The armies of the Thirty Years' War typically were about two-thirds

8. Eberhard von Wassenberg, *Erneuerter Teutscher Florus* (1647). Gustav Könnecke, *Quellen und Forschungen zur Lebensgeschichte Grimmelshausens*, ed. Jan Hendrik Scholte (Weimar, 1926 and 1928), I, 3 ff. places Grimmelshausen's historical statements in Courage and those in Wassenberg side by side.

infantry and one-third cavalry, with some artillery. Two types of soldiers, pikemen and musketeers, made up the infantry. A pikeman wore a helmet and a breastplate and carried a sword and a pike some twenty feet long. The musketeer was armed with a musket, a firearm about six feet long which discharged balls weighing about five ounces; he carried a bandoleer with extra powder charges and a "fork" on which the musket barrel was rested during firing. The cavalry, which was the preferred service, was divided into light, heavy, and irregular. Heavy cavalry consisted of cuirassiers, who wore full armor and carried a sword and a brace of pistols, and of lancers, who carried a lance in addition to side arms. The light cavalry were harquebusiers. They wore armor only from the waist up and were armed with two pistols and a harquebus, a firearm lighter and of smaller caliber than a musket, which was carried on a bandoleer. The irregular cavalry—the Croats, the Stradiotes, and the Hussars—were armed with weapons peculiar to their nations. The dragoon—part light cavalryman and part foot soldier—carried a musket and pistols, and could fight either on horseback or dismounted. During this period the dragoons were classed as infantry.

The largest regular military unit in both the infantry and cavalry was the regiment, which was commanded by a colonel, the man who recruited and equipped it. The regimental officers under him were the lieutenant colonel and the major. In theory an Imperial infantry regiment consisted of ten companies of 300—120 pikemen, 160 musketeers, and 20 halberdiers. Each company was commanded by a captain of infantry appointed by the colonel; the captain, in turn, appointed the company grade officers—a lieutenant and an ensign, or sublieutenant. The company noncommissioned officers were sergeants and corporals, as they are today; and the men were divided into regular foot soldiers and "exempts" (*Gefreite*), so called because they were exempt from guard duty. Even in theory the cavalry regiment varied in size and composition. In the Imperial army it generally numbered five hundred to a thousand troopers, and was made up of three to eight companies which ranged in size from around sixty to two hundred, depending on the type of cavalry. The cavalry company was under the command of a captain of horse and two company grade officers, a lieutenant and an ensign, or cornet.

For every fighting man there were three or four or even five non-combatants who were attached or had attached themselves to the army. In addition to provosts, quartermasters, surgeons, and chaplains, there were the sutlers, hawkers, and commissary butchers who supplied provisions; pages and menials who served the officers; the "rabble"— half-grown youths who tended the horses of the common soldiers, carried their armor and baggage, and stole for them; and, finally, officers' ladies, the wives and children of the common soldiers, and whores and camp followers. A regiment of three thousand men sometimes had as many as three hundred wagons in its baggage train.

Wherever an army went it brought poverty and ruin. If a city or territory resisted and was taken, the conquering troops usually were allowed to plunder, rape, and murder at will. When an area permitted itself to be occupied by an army, its residents found in their midst an all-devouring organism over which they had no control. Military personnel were not subject to civil law and could be tried and executed only by a court-martial. A soldier could not even be executed on the town gallows; he had to be hanged on a "quarter gallows" by an army hangman, who, unlike the civilian executioner, was considered "honorable."

Grimmelshausen's sympathies are with the common soldier and his cohorts, male and female, and it is of them rather than of the officer caste that he chooses to write. He never permits his heroine to marry a man above the rank of captain of horse, and he clearly indicates his feelings about high-ranking officers by making Courage's particular enemies and detractors a major and a lieutenant colonel.

IV

The figure of Courage, although much more limited in scope than that of Simplicissimus, is perhaps the most unified and strongest of all Grimmelshausen's creations. She emerges as a rounded and consistent human being, capable of holding our interest and rousing our sympathy in a different, even more personal way than Simplicissimus, who often is too obviously an abstraction and a vehicle for the author's pronouncements. That Courage exists for us as a flesh-and-blood woman is the more surprising since she too receives the traditional seventeenth-century treatment and her story is told within an allegorical framework. Underlying the tale of the adventuress and courtesan are three typically Baroque themes: The first deals with the dangers of disturbing the harmony of nature; the second argues the proposition *mulier non homo* (women are not properly human beings); and the third demonstrates the vanity of the finite world. Viewing the book as a whole, the heroine's life history constitutes an allegory on the nature of courage and what this much lauded virtue does for and to a man of action.

In Courage's case, the harmony of nature has been violated from the very moment of her conception. As the child of an illicit union between a high-ranking nobleman and a maid of honor at his wife's court, she is deprived of parental love and the company of her peers and is brought up by a lowborn woman of questionable morals. Forced to wear male clothing and act the part of a boy, she learns to fight like a soldier and—what is worse—to enjoy it; in her own words, "from childhood on it was my nature to like things best when they were all topsy-turvy" (p. 36). Because she has been denied the opportunity to behave as a normal girl, she grows up uncertain of her role and with little understanding of her own nature. She realizes only that she is able to wield great power over men and that she is possessed by insatiable and unbridled cravings for the gratification of the flesh and the amassing of material wealth. As she acquires the masculine vices she loses all her feminine characteristics except the ability to seduce men; so warped is her nature that at one time her "most fervent wish" is to become a man or at least to simulate a state as close to manhood as possible—"I often thought of pretending to be a hermaphrodite, to see whether this way I might gain the right to wear trousers in public and pass for a young fellow" (p. 67).

Courage's moral and spiritual failures are linked to the second theme of *mulier non homo*. "Long, long ago," says Courage, "when I was in the bloom of youth and the state of innocence, my dear reverent sirs, was the time to set me on the path [of repentance and Christian virtue]" (pp. 33–4). If man is the only being truly created in the image of God, then it is his responsibility to lead the weaker sex on the path of righteousness. Courage's men fail to fulfill this responsibility not only because of her "unnaturalness" but because of their own sinfulness. It is perhaps the most serious fault of Simplicissimus that he who tells of his own conversion and search for salvation was unable to resist the charms of this fallen woman, much less attempt her correction. The *mulier non homo* theme also explains in part Courage's sometimes surprising insensitiveness, her apparent inability to feel deeply humiliation and pain. In Grimmelshausen's view—a view which was quite prevalent in his day—

> Women weep with moans and sighs,
> But see! their tears are only lies,
> For they but feign that they fare ill:
> Women can weep when e'er they will (p. 58).

Courage does indeed feel, but alas most of her emotions are evil ones—rage, vengefulness, hatred, malice, greed, and lust. Only occasionally is there a glimmer of a softer emotion, permitting us a glimpse of the woman she might have been. For Courage is fashioned after a grand design.

This leads us into the third theme—the vanity of the world. In this context Courage—the beautiful and beguiling enchantress of men, the ever young and maidenly who brings riches and love to him who possesses her—becomes the symbol for our finite world, the antithesis of the world of the Beyond. This visible world must be shown for what it really is—a sham, an illusion, a poor shadow of the true, infinite, and eternal world of the Hereafter. Thus as the action unfolds, Courage is gradually unmasked, gradually stripped of her glamour, until we lose sight of her as an old gypsy queen who has blackened her face and no longer makes any pretense at allurement.

The ambiguity of her name in itself expresses the shifting, unreal, and illusory quality of the world she personifies. In German *Courasche* is army slang, a rough equivalent of the English word *guts*, denoting the raw physical courage of the male animal. This soldier's term for a virtue particularly associated with men of action, but here applied to a woman, connotes an earthiness, even a vulgarity, in German which it is impossible to render into English without losing many word plays and considerably weakening its symbolical force. The name receives a special ambiguity because it is employed as a euphemism for the physical attribute which Courage—being a woman, not a man—does not possess. Only Courage and her lover know what the name actually refers to; the world at large interprets it in its primary conventional sense. The implied paradox is the first step toward a discussion of the ambivalent character of woman and ultimately of the world. But quite apart from the metaphysical implications of the name, its application to a woman slyly discredits the popular image of the he-man.

Finally there is the allegory on courage. It is shown to be a dangerous virtue. It brings riches and fame, the approbation and envy of one's fellows. Any man may possess courage but to him who makes a habit of it, who binds it to himself as a husband does his wife, it ultimately brings death. So in Grimmelshausen's tale all Courage's husbands die except Hopalong, and after what she has made of him he might as well be dead.

V

In our own day Grimmelshausen's heroine has reappeared in a modern masterpiece, Bertolt Brecht's drama of the Thirty Years' War, *Mother Courage and Her Children.*[9] The play opens in 1624. Mother Courage is a camp follower who ekes out a living for herself and her children selling provisions to both armies. She is first seen as a middle-aged woman riding with her daughter, a mute, on her sutler's wagon which is pulled by her two sons. In a series of episodes, each complete in itself, we are shown Courage's vain efforts to shield her children from the hazards of war. One son dies because he is too courageous, the other because he is too honest, and the daughter because she is too compassionate. In all three cases it is their mother's avarice that dooms them.

The Baroque age and its great calamity, the Thirty Years' War, seem to have held a special attraction for German authors of later generations, and it is interesting to note that during the period in which Brecht wrote and produced his drama (roughly 1937–1941) more than a score of literary works about the Thirty Years' War appeared in Germany. Certainly the writings of Grimmelshausen were a part of Brecht's heritage, and Grimmelshausen's heroine was the direct inspiration of his own. A comparison of the two views of the same figure will illuminate the differences and similarities in the authors' attitude, emphasis, and judgment, and thus may afford a deeper understanding of both works.

The name of Brecht's character is Anna Fierling but, like her predecessor, she is known as Courage and in her case, too, the sobriquet is ambiguous. As she explains it:

9. Bertolt Brecht, *Mutter Courage und ihre Kinder: Eine Chronik aus dem Dreizigjährigen Krieg* (Berlin: Suhrkamp Verlag, 1957). Page references in the text are to this edition. For an excellent brief discussion of Brecht's Epic theatre, see Eric Bentley, *In Search of Theatre* (New York: Alfred A. Knopf, Inc., 1953), pp. 144–160.

> They call me Mother Courage, Sergeant, because I was afraid I'd be ruined, so I drove through the bombardment of Riga with fifty loaves of bread in my cart. It was high time, they were getting moldy, I didn't have a choice (p. 9).

On the surface, this can be taken as the bland understatement of a single-minded tradeswoman who sees things in their true light and shies away from any heroic posturing, but basically it is curiously similar to the anecdote concerning the genesis of the earlier Courage's name (p. 44). What Grimmelshausen conveys euphemistically and non-literally Brecht expresses in his heroine's paradoxical statement on a literal meaning of courage. According to this statement, Mother Courage, too, is named for what she is not: "They call me Mother Courage . . . because I was afraid I'd be ruined." If her next words—"so I drove through the bombardment"—seem to weaken the irony, then the conclusion of her next sentence—"I didn't have a choice"—restores its strength. Neither woman seems willing to admit that courage, the quality which each possesses so abundantly in the primary meaning of the word, is worth taking seriously.

While it is clear that Brecht joins with Grimmelshausen in taking a skeptical view of the conventional concept of heroism, a comparison of the two Courages reveals that they differ in several important respects. In the first place, Grimmelshausen's heroine never bears a child. (This, in fact, is the crux of the fraud she perpetrates on Simplicissimus. Gloatingly she recounts how she tricks him into believing that the chambermaid's illegitimate offspring is their son, the fruit of her barren womb.) [10] All through her life Courage is essentially the "strange woman," the illicit mate and seducer, the succubus, whose

10. Simplicissimus' version is as follows: "During the same hour in which my wife was delivered of a child our serving maid was also brought to bed, and the child which she brought forth looked like me, while the one my wife bore was the spitting image of our farmhand; to top it all, the above-mentioned lady [Courage] had a child laid on my doorstep during the same night with a written message that I was the father, so that all at once I had three children, making me fear that more might crawl out of every corner, which gave me quite a few gray

companionship imperils man's soul. Nothing is less in keeping with her character than the tender and binding sentiments of motherhood. To Courage her beautiful but sterile body exists for the irresponsible gratification of lust, and she glories in the fact that it can be used to give her power over men and to gain her riches.

A second difference is that Courage is of noble birth. This is a variation on the picaresque tradition: as originally conceived the picaresque hero or heroine is a baseborn individual whose amoral conduct in manifold tawdry, criminal, and preposterous adventures provides the focal point for satire. Grimmelshausen deepens the satire by making his heroine of noble lineage, for far from serving as a spur to virtue or even as a deterrent to vice, to Courage it is nothing but a means to an end, like her physical charms; it is something she sloughs off, disregards, as soon as her beauty is gone. It may also be that Grimmelshausen endowed Courage with high birth to account for some of her admirable qualities and to emphasize the pitifulness and depth of her self-induced degradation. At any rate, the mere fact that he is concerned with her parentage helps to demonstrate what is perhaps the main difference in the two authors' treatment of the character. Whereas Brecht shows us Mother Courage only in the second half of her life, Grimmelshausen follows the course of his heroine from childhood to old age. During a lifetime easily spanning the Biblical three score and ten, Courage presents an ever-changing image to the reader. This continuous change, deriving not from the heroine's character but from external circumstance—that is, the variability of fortune—is another illustration of the vanity-of-the-world theme.

Since Brecht's Mother Courage is portrayed as a sutler, the period in her predecessor's life when she engages in the sutler's trade affords a

---

hairs. But that's the way it goes if one gives in to his bestial lusts and leads as godless and wicked a life as I once did.

"There was no other way; I was obliged to hold three christenings, and in the bargain the town magistrate punished me for the crime of fornication . . ." (*Der Abentheurliche Simplicissimus*, Book V, Chapter 9).

good opportunity for comparing the two figures; moreover, some important facets of the first Courage's character are revealed in her account of why she decides to go into business (Chapter 15). Now approaching middle age she is still very beautiful and still has her heart set on being an officer's lady. Her avarice is aroused when she sees what profits come the sutler's way, and she begins to ponder how she might start a sutlery herself. The loss of status involved in such a step—from being the widow of a captain of horse she would "sink to the rank of a sutler's woman"—at first deters her, but when she reflects that "many an honest officer [is] obliged to pull in his belt" while the sutler continues to rake in gold pieces, she is able to face the loss of status with equanimity. Hardheaded practicality—and an eye to the possibility of regaining her former social position at some future time—govern the arrangements she makes with Hopalong, her lover and partner in the sutlery. By the terms of a contract she compels him to sign, although he plays the role of her husband and the ostensible head of the business in effect he is nothing but her slave and she has entire control of the pursestrings. As a further safeguard for her good name, her old foster mother will serve as duenna. Thus, under a double blanket of respectability, Courage not only can satisfy her avarice but also is free to indulge her dissolute and lustful instincts as a prostitute. But the most significant point to be brought out about this lopsided partnership between the highborn adventuress and the simple musketeer is the reason for its ultimate failure, which lies in Courage's own character. She is incapable of sustaining any relationship based on reciprocity or mutual respect: she must always be the dominant one.

The same autocratic and domineering nature is found in Brecht's Mother Courage. She differs, as we have seen, in being of lowly birth, in being a mother, and in being presented only in the second half of her life. Also, she is possessed of neither Courage's beauty nor her grand, sophisticated manner; although she may be promiscuous she is certainly not a prostitute; and she is never subject to so great a diversity of fortune as her opposite number. But no less than the other Courage she tyrannizes over those close to her. While she cares for her children and the lesser figures, like the chaplain and the cook, who are drawn into her orbit, she does not scruple to use them as she sees fit. The two Courages are also alike in their tremendous vitality, their great strength, and their singleness of purpose, which enable them to endure terrible hardships with fortitude and to take setbacks in their stride. They waste no time bewailing their fate; again and again, they bounce back with almost superhuman resilience and resume their unswerving, tireless pursuit of their aims. Avarice is the mainspring of their strength. Down-to-earth, soberly practical, guileful, unsentimental and single-minded, the war to them is a business opportunity, a stage for their operations, and nothing else. Neither is concerned with larger meanings or the state of the world, and both are completely honest about their determination to make use of the war for their own ends. If Mother Courage's plan lacks the scope of Courage's, certainly she shows the same dogged determination. More importantly, although their insight into their condition varies in degree, the character of neither woman is changed by the calamities of warfare. To be sure, Mother Courage at one point curses the war, but as Brecht says in his notes to the play, she "sees some things" only—she has but a fleeting glimpse of her own plight. As for Courage, Siegfried Streller in a perceptive analysis, points out that up to Chapter 13 there is a recognizable desire on her part to lead a respectable life; it is only after this that she begins to revenge herself on the male sex.[11] But the reason for this development, which is inherent in her character, can be seen from the beginning; and nowhere is there any mention of piety, repentance, or reform.

We find, then, that although outwardly diverging in many respects, inwardly Courage and Mother Courage are closely related. Moreover, despite the difference in their situations, both awaken our compassion. Mother Courage in her dumb grief for her children takes on tragic proportions, and though the other Courage may exasperate and repel us, underneath her lusty, sardonic, dissolute exterior she too is a victim for whom we feel pity and to whom we cannot deny sympathy.

11. *Grimmelshausens Simplicianische Schriften* (Berlin: Neus Beiträge zur Literaturwissenschaft, 1957).

As a final parallel, each woman is left with nothing but the naked symbol of her life's activity. Having lost her children, forsaken by her friends, Mother Courage stumbles along in the tracks of war, dragging her sutler's cart. Similarly, Courage, the outcast gypsy, having lost her beauty and her claim, however tenuous, to a place in respectable society is left with nothing but her lump of gold. The lump of gold symbolizes the crux of Grimmelshausen's message. This worldly wealth, the visible, physical, and finite harvest which is Courage's gain on earth, this noblest of the metals, is a fitting counterpart for the most precious possession in that other world, the invisible realm of the infinite: for the sake of the gold, Courage has given up her chance for eternal salvation. In Brecht's play the central symbol is of quite a different order. The sutler's cart is the instrument by which Mother Courage hopes to acquire riches in the finite world, and she has retained it at the expense of the very reason for her using it: her family and their earthly happiness.

The two symbols reveal the very significant differences between the two authors and their treatment of the problem. On one level, that of the finite world, the "here and now," Grimmelshausen's heroine is a success and Brecht's a failure. With Mother Courage the means is the sutler's cart, the desired end is happiness in the finite world, the actual end is negation of happiness in this world. With Courage the means are her natural endowment and the life she leads—the lump of gold is both the desired end and the actual end. But Grimmelshausen adds another dimension, the infinite and the eternal, and in this dimension Courage fails completely and irrevocably. Brecht's finite world (the "here and now") has as its counterpart only by implication another finite world, tomorrow's world, the "here and then." In this world Mother Courage would be a success, for in this better world she would have no opportunity and no need to pursue the wrong course. It is the cart and what it stands for, namely, a wrong human activity and a wrong human institution, which make the better world impossible for Mother Courage. This shabby, mobile, but lifeless appendage also symbolizes the treatment of the problem by the author. Just as technique and not abstract values, the means and not the end, have become the important point, so what is wrong with this world can only be shown by the absence of what is good, what is beautiful, and what is worthwhile. Instead what is shown are stupid, vicious, deceitful or ineffective actions. Goodness, beauty, and truth are, so to say, the ethereal spaces in between the ugly solid forms of the wrong "here and now." The right world, that of tomorrow, is perceived in its very absence. Yet it is merely a later stage of the "here and now" and thought of in the terms of a finite world, whether today's or tomorrow's.

The two symbols thus represent both authors' dialectics and dicta. The finite world is rejected in both cases. In Grimmelshausen's work its seductive glamor is painted in vivid colors in order to be unmasked and discredited gradually and finally. In Brecht's work the finite world is mercilessly exhibited again and again for what it is. With Grimmelshausen the symbol represents the wrong end; with Brecht it represents the wrong means. With both the heroine fails.

But on an entirely different level one might say that both Courage and Mother Courage succeed. And it is to the credit of both authors— the seventeenth-century Christian and the twentieth-century Communist—that from different points in time and from radically different points of view they have evoked the human image in its piteous condition, flayed, dishonored, and condemned, but of unsurpassed grandeur in its stubborn and errant persistence, in its perverse and prevailing courage.

ROBERT L. HILLER

JOHN C. OSBORNE

The editions used in the translation are: *Grimmelshausen Simplicianische Schriften*, ed. Alfred Kelletat (Munich: Winkler-Verlag, 1956); *Grimmelshausens Courasche*, ed. J. H. Scholte (Halle: Neudrucke Deutscher Literatur Werke, 1923); and *Grimmelshausens Werke*, ed. Hans Heinrich Borcherdt (Berlin: Bongs Klassiker, o. J, 1922).

The Runagate Courage

True Cause and Briefly Told Contents
of This Little Tract

After the gypsy woman Courage learns from *lib. 5 cap.* 6 of *Simplicissimi* story of his life that he has spoken of her to her dishonor, she becomes so embittered at him that to spite him, but to her own shame (with which, however, she is little concerned, because after joining the gypsies she has renounced all honor and virtue itself), she brings to light her whole lewdly led career, in order to ruin the aforesaid *Simplicissimum* in the eyes of the world, because he was not loath to defile himself with such a loose harlot as she confesses herself to be, and in truth has been, and even boasted of his lewdness and evil; from which must be concluded that neither horse nor nag, neither knave nor whore, is one hair better than the other; in the bargain she nicely rubs in how masterfully she cheated him and paid him back in return.

Chapter 1

Complete and much needed prefatory note, to explain for whose sake and whose pleasure and for what pressing reasons the old archfraud, runagate, and gypsy Courage tells and thereby exposes to full view of the whole world her wondrous and right strange life history

Well! (you will say, gentlemen) who would ever have thought that the old fool would ever presume to escape the impending wrath of God? What's behind it all? Why, she simply must! The gamboling days of her youth are over, her wantonness and impertinence have gone to rest, her burdened and affrighted conscience has awakened and she has fallen prey now to irksome old age, which is ashamed to let her continue in her former overwhelming folly and is mortified and disgusted at the prospect of continuing to keep past misdeeds buried in her heart. The old crowbait is finally beginning to see and feel that certain death will soon come knocking at her door and will extort from her that last breath of life on which she must inevitably journey to another world, where she will be obliged to render an exact accounting of all her deeds and misdeeds here below; this is why, before the eyes of the whole world, she is beginning to disburden her old ass[1] of the overwhelming burden of its troubles, to see whether she can perhaps relieve herself by that much, so that she may gather fresh hope of attaining heavenly mercy even at this late date. Yes, my dear sirs! That is what you will say. But others will think: Could Courage really venture to imagine that she can whiten her old wrinkled skin, having smeared it with ointment for *morbus gallicus*[2] during her

1. *her old ass*] herself and referring to the mule which she rides.
2. *morbus gallicus*] syphilis.

youth, then with all kinds of Italian and Spanish cosmetics, and finally with Egyptian louse ointment and much goosefat, this skin now smoked black by the campfire, this skin so often compelled to change its color? Could she really think that she will be able to empty her heart of her villainy and past depravities by thus giving a full accounting of them, and that she may also be able to erase the deeply etched wrinkles from her wicked brow, thus changing it once more into its former smooth state of childlike innocence? Could this old slut, now that she has not one but both feet in the grave—if she even be worthy of a grave—this old woman (you will say) who has wallowed all her life in all kinds of infamy and vice, who is burdened down with more wicked deeds than years, more whorish capers than months, more thievish tricks than weeks, more mortal sins than days, and more venial sins than hours, she who, old as she is, never had nary a thought of conversion, could she really now venture to make her peace with God? Does she actually imagine that she might still be in time to set things aright, now that through pangs of conscience she is beginning to suffer hellish pain and torture which outweighs all the delights of the flesh she tasted and enjoyed during her whole life? Well! If this useless and decrepit encumbrance and burden on the good earth had wallowed only in delights of the flesh and not also in all manner of arch-vices, indeed if she had not gone and sunk into the deepest abyss of evil, then perhaps she might still be granted the grace to harbor some faint hope for mercy.

Yes, my good sirs! That is what you will say and that is what you will think, and therefore you will be astounded when the news of this, my great and general confession, reaches your ears; and I, when I hear of your astonishment, I will forget my age and either laugh myself young again or laugh myself sick! Why that, Courage? Why will you laugh like that? For this reason: That you think an old woman who has enjoyed life so well for so long and who imagines that her soul has, so to speak, grown fast to her body should be thinking of death; that such a woman as you know me to be and to have been all my life should be thinking of saving her soul; and that she who, so the priests tell me, has trod a path bent straight for hell her whole life long should only now be thinking of heaven. I candidly confess that I cannot decide either to equip myself for the journey which the priests are trying to persuade me to take, or to give up that which, according to them, blocks my path; since for this journey I lack one thing and have too much of several, in particular two things. What I lack is repentance, and what I should lack but do not is avarice and envy.[3] If I hated my lump of gold, which I have scraped together at risk of life and limb, indeed, as I have been told, at the cost of eternal salvation, as much as I envy my neighbor, and if I loved my neighbor as dearly as I do my money, then perhaps the heavenly gift of repentance might indeed follow; I know about the nature of the various ages through which every woman passes, and by my own example I confirm: You cannot teach an old dog new tricks. My choler[4] has grown with the years, and I cannot rid myself of my gall the way a butcher turns a sow's stomach inside out to clean it; how then should I be able to resist wrath? Who is going to evacuate my overwhelming excess of phlegm and cure me of my phlegma? Who will free me of my melancholy humor and with it my inclination to envy? Who will persuade me to hate my ducats, when I know from experience, after all, that they can save me from want and be the only consolation of my old age? Long,

3. *avarice and envy*] two of the Seven Deadly Sins. Courage, in the course of her biography makes clear that she is also guilty of four of the remaining five: pride, intemperance, wrath, and lust. Sloth is the only one to which she seems not to have fallen prey, although from the account of her life among the gypsies as it appears in *Hopalong* it might be argued that she also commits this sin. (See Appendix 2, *Hopalong*, Chapter 6.)

4. *choler*] in the seventeenth century it was believed that the health and disposition of man was determined by four humors, or body fluids: blood, phlegm, choler, and melancholy (also called "black choler"). An excess of yellow choler, which was bile and produced by the gall, was supposed to cause irascibility; blood was considered the vital fluid and the seat of the passions (anger and lust); phlegm, thought to be a cold and moist fluid, was believed to induce sluggishness and coldness and dullness of character; melancholy or black choler (black bile), was thought to cause sullenness and gloominess.

long ago, when I was in the bloom of youth and the state of innocence, my dear reverent sirs, was the time to set me on the path which, according to you, I am only now beginning to tread; for though I was at that time entering upon the path of titillating temptation, it would still have been easier for me to withstand the sanguine impulse than to now withstand the onslaught of the other three worst humors. Therefore, go to such youth as have hearts not yet soiled like Courage's with other images, and teach, admonish, beg, even implore them not to go so far astray for want of discretion as poor Courage has.

But listen, Courage, if you are not considering mending your ways, then why do you desire to tell your life story as if in confession and reveal to all the world your vices? I am doing it to spite Simplicissimo,[5] because I cannot avenge myself on him any other way; for after this nasty *vocativus*[6] put me in the family way (*scilicet*)[7] in Sauerbrunnen[8] and afterwards rid himself of me by a shameful trick, he then goes and proclaims to the whole world in his pretty biography my disgrace and his own; but I, for my part, shall tell him now what kind of honorable minx he was dealing with, so that he may know of what he bragged and may perhaps wish that he had kept silent about our *Historii*; by which, however, the whole reputable world may learn that just as horse and nag, just so whore and knave, are of the same breed and neither one a hair better than the other. Like will to like, as the devil said to the collier, and sins and sinners are generally punished by other sins and sinners.

5. *Simplicissimo*] Simplicissimus (also Simplicius), the hero of Grimmelshausen's novel of the same name. The latin case-endings are used consistently throughout. See Introduction.

6. *vocativus*] a sly rogue.

7. *scilicet*] of course (meant ironically since it actually did not happen).

8. *Sauerbrunnen*] literally, a mineral spring; not an actual place-name.

Chapter 2

Maid Libushka[1] *(hereafter called Courage) enters the war, calls herself Janco, and must for a time serve as a valet-de-chambre, whereby it is reported how she acted and what other strange things happened to her*

Those who know how the Slavonic peoples treat their serfs might possibly think that I was bred and born of a Bohemian nobleman and a peasant's daughter. But knowing and thinking are two different things. I think a lot of things too, but I still do not know. If I were to say that I had known who my parents were, I should be lying, and it would not be the first time; but this I do know: That I was brought up tenderly enough in Prachatitz,[2] kept in school, and instructed more carefully than a girl of humble birth in sewing, knitting, embroidery, and other such lady's work. Ample money for my board came from my father, but just what place it came from I still did not know; and my mother wrote often and inquired about my welfare, though I never met her face to face either. When the Bavarian prince[3] marched with Bucquoy into Bohemia to drive the new king[4] out again, I was an impertinent thing of thirteen years who was beginning to have all kinds of fancies and conceits about where I might have come from; and that was my greatest concern, because I could not ask, and on my own I could not get to the bottom of it at all. I was guarded from

1. *Libushka*] Libussa, name of the legendary founder of Prague.
2. *Prachatitz*] in the Bohemian forest.
3. *Bavarian prince*] Duke Maximilian Emanuel of Bavaria (1573–1651). Grimmelshausen's historical source was Wassenberg: *Erneuerter teutscher Florus* (Frankfurt, 1647). See Introduction.
4. *new king*] Frederick V, Prince-Elector of the Palatinate, the so-called "Winter King."

common folk as a beautiful painting is protected from dust; my nurse kept constant watch over me, and because I was not allowed to play with other girls my age, look you, the bees which curiosity hatched in my bonnet increased in number, and they were the only things I concerned myself about anyway.

Now when the Duke of Bavaria separated from Bucquoy, the Bavarian moved before Budweis[5] and the latter before Prachatitz. Budweis soon surrendered and was very wise to do so, but Prachatitz held out and felt the might of Imperial arms, which dealt cruelly with the zealots. Now as soon as my nurse got wind of the way things were going, she said to me right away: "Maid Libushka, if you wish to keep your maidenhead, you must let me shear your head and put you in men's clothes; if not, I would not give the buckle off a chastity belt for your honor, which has been commended so earnestly to my care."

I thought: "What strange talk is this?" But she fetched shears and cut off my golden hair on the right side, but she left the other side be, so that in every way my hair was like the most elegant men were wearing it then.

"There, my daughter," she said, "if you escape this tumult with your honor intact, you will still have enough hair to adorn you, and in a year the rest will grow back in too."

I was quick to let her console me, for from childhood on it was my nature to like things best when they were all topsy-turvy, and when she had dressed me in breeches and a doublet she taught me to take longer strides and what other mannerisms I should affect. Thus we waited for the Imperial army to invade the city, my nurse with fear and trembling, to be sure, but I was lusting to see what new and uncommon carnival this might turn out to be. I soon found out; but I will not delay my tale by recounting how the men of the captured

5. The united armies first took Budweis (on the river Moldau in southern Bohemia) on September 11, 1620. Then Maximilian moved against Wodnian, Bucquoy against Prachatitz, which was taken after heavy resistance. Almost 1500 people were slain in the city.

city were slaughtered by the conquerors, the women raped, and the city itself plundered, since such things were so common in the recent, long-continuing war that everyone has a tale to tell about them. But I am bound to report, if indeed I am to tell my whole history, that a German trooper took me along as his boy, to take care of his horses and to help him forage, that is, steal. I called myself Janco, and I could speak German pretty well, but, as is the custom with all us Bohemians, I did not let on that I did; otherwise, I was slender and pretty and had a noble air; and I only wish that whoever does not believe me had seen me fifty years ago, because he would surely have to attest that it was so.

Now when this first master of mine brought me to the company, his captain of horse, who was truly a brave and handsome young gentleman, asked him what he intended to do with me. He answered: "What other troopers do with their boys: Have him steal and take care of my horses; I hear that for this the Bohemians are said to be the best. They say it is certain that when a Bohemian takes oakum out of a house a German will surely not find any flax in it."

"But," answered my captain of horse, "what if he works this Bohemian craft on you first and rides off with your horses as proof?"

"I'll keep my eye on him, all right," said the trooper, "till I get him out of his own backyard."

"Farm boys who have been brought up with horses," answered the captain of horse, "make much better stableboys than town boys who cannot learn in a city how to take care of a horse. Besides, it seems to me that this lad is of a good family and much too daintily brought up to take care of a trooper's horses."

I pricked up my ears mightily, without letting on that I understood anything of their discourse, because they were speaking German; my greatest concern was that I might be turned out and chased back to the plundered city of Prachatitz, because I had not yet had my fill of the drums and pipes, the cannon and trumpets, sounds that made my heart leap for joy. Finally it came to pass, I know not whether for good or ill, that the captain of horse kept me for himself, to wait upon his person as a page and valet-de-chambre; to the trooper, however, he gave another Bohemian clodhopper for a boy, because the trooper insisted on having a thief from our nation.

Well, I fitted quite nicely into my new role in this masquerade. I was able to fawn over my captain of horse so cunningly, keep his clothes so clean, do up his white linen so nicely, and care for his person so well that he could not but regard me as the epitome of a good valet-de-chambre; and because I also had a great liking for arms, I took care of his in such manner that my master and his servants could rely on them, and therefore I soon got him to give me a sword and to dub me fit for military service by giving me a cuff on the ear. That I behaved so sturdily in this could not but surprise everyone, and they all thought it a sign of incomparable intelligence that I learned to speak German so quickly, because no one knew that I had been obliged to learn it from childhood on. Next, I tried my best to rid myself of all my feminine ways and to acquire masculine ones instead; I purposely learned to curse like a trooper and to drink like a tinker besides. I drank many a cup to everlasting friendship with those whom I thought my equals, and whenever I wished to swear that something I said was true, I did it with rogues' and thieves' curses, so that no one might remark wherein I had fallen short at birth or what, for that matter, I had not brought along into the world with me at all.

Chapter 3

While serving with a resolute captain of horse Janco exchanges his noble hymen for the nomen Courage

My captain of horse, as noted above, was a handsome young gentleman, a good horseman, a good swordsman, a good dancer, a cavalier, and a soldier, and uncommonly fond of the chase; in particular, to course the hare with hounds was his greatest joy. He had no more beard on his face than I, and if he had worn lady's dress not one in a thousand but would have taken him for a beautiful maiden. But where am I off to? I must tell my history. After Budweis and Prachatitz had fallen, both armies marched before Pilsen, which resisted bravely, to be sure, but afterwards received its punishment too, with pitiable slaughter and hangings; from there they moved on Rakonitz, where there occurred the first action on the open field which I had ever seen; and at that time I wished I were a man, so I could go to war all my life; for everything that happened was so merry that my heart leaped for joy, and this desire was increased by the battle on the White Hill[1] near Prague, because our side won a great victory and lost few men. At that time my captain of horse took much booty, but I did not let him use me as a page or valet, much less as a girl, but as a soldier who has sworn to go against the enemy and earns his pay by doing so.

After the encounter, the Duke of Bavaria marched into Austria, the Prince Elector of Saxony[2] into Lusatia and our General Bucquoy into Moravia, to force the rebels against the Emperor to renew their

1. *White Hill*] in the vicinity of Prague, where the Duke of Bavaria and Bucquoy, the Imperial general, defeated the "Winter King" on November 8, 1620. The story therefore begins in this year and Courage must have been born in 1607.

2. *Prince-Elector of Saxony*] John George, Elector of Saxony (1611–1656).

allegiance to him; and while the latter was having himself cured of injuries that he had received before Rakonitz, during this same lull between battles which we were enjoying on his account, look you, I received a wound in my heart, which was pierced by the charm of my captain of horse, for I observed in him only those qualities which I have recounted above and paid no heed to the fact that he could neither read nor write and was altogether such a crude person that I can swear on my faith that I never heard or saw him in prayer. And even if wise King Alphonsus[3] himself had called him a beautiful *bestia*, it would not have quenched my ardor, which, however, I thought to keep secret, because what little maidenly modesty I had left cautioned me to do so; but this I was able to do only with the greatest impatience, so that in spite of my youth, which made me not yet fit for any man, I often wished I could take the place of those whom I and others at times procured for him.

In the beginning I was in no small measure kept from a violent and dangerous outburst of passion by the fact that my beloved was born of a noble and renowned family, which made me imagine that he would wed no one who did not even know her own parents; and I could not make up my mind to become his mistress, because every day with the army I saw so many whores turned over to the rabble.[4] Now although this war and strife which was going on inside me tortured me dreadfully, I was nevertheless at the same time lusty and gay, indeed I was of such a nature that my spirits were dampened by neither the desire within me nor the work and unrest of war without. To be sure, I did not have anything to do but wait upon my captain of horse, but love taught me to accomplish that with such industry and zeal that my master would have sworn a thousand oaths that there was no more

3. *King Alphonsus*] Alfonso X, King of Leon and Castile (1252–1284), called the Wise, philosopher and astronomer who devised the planetary tables which bore his name.

4. *turned over to the rabble*] this inhuman punishment meted out by the military to women of immoral character resulted in the death of the poor wretches under the most appalling circumstances.

1. A Cavalry Commander. From *Capricci.* 1621

faithful servant on earth than I; in all engagements, no matter how sharp they may have been, I never moved from his side or left his back unguarded, though I was not obliged to serve him thus; and on top of that, I was always willing to do anything at all which I knew would please him. Thus, he could have read from my face easily enough that I honored and worshiped him with far greater devotion than that of a common servant if only my clothes had not deceived him. In the meantime, the more time passed, the bigger my bosom grew and the more the shoe pinched me, in such manner that I did not trust myself to conceal much longer either my bosom, which would soon show without, or the fire which was raging within it.

After we had stormed Iglau,[5] subdued Trebits, brought Znaim to its knees, bent Bruenn and Olmuetz under the yoke, and forced most of the other cities to submit to us, I shared in a good deal of the booty, which my captain of horse gave me as a gift in return for my faithful services and with which I equipped myself excellently well, got myself the best possible mount, stuffed my own purse, and at times drank a measure of wine with other soldiers at the sutler's.

Once I was making merry with a few of them who out of envy directed abusive words at me, and there was one in particular among them who was hostile toward me and who reviled and scorned the Bohemian nation quite to excess. This fool represented to me that the Bohemians had mistaken the rotten maggotty carcass of a dog for a stinking cheese and had gulped it down; and he even mocked me as if I personally had been present at the feast; therefore both of us came to cursewords, from cursewords to blows, and from blows to scuffling and wrestling, during which work my adversary whisked his hand inside my trousers to seize me by that equipment which I, after all, did not possess, which futile but murderous hold vexed me much more than if he had not found himself empty-handed; and for this very reason I became that much more enraged, indeed nearly half out of my

5. Iglau, Trebitz, Znaim, Bruenn, and Olmuetz are cities in Moravia which were taken by Bucquoy in 1621.

senses, as it were, so that I summoned up all my strength and agility and defended myself by scratching, biting, hitting, and kicking in such a way that I brought my enemy down and so used his face that it resembled a devil's mask more than a human countenance; I should have throttled him too, in fact, if the rest of the company had not torn me from him and made peace. I got off with nothing but a black eye and could well imagine that this evil customer had become quite aware of my true sex, and I believe too that he would have revealed it, if he had not been afraid either that he would receive more blows, or that in addition to those already received he would be made a laughingstock for letting a girl beat him; and because I was worried that he still might gossip, look you, I departed.

When I got to our quarters my captain of horse was not at home, but in the company of other officers, with whom he was making merry and where he learned, before I came before him, what kind of battle I had fought. He loved me, knowing me to be a resolute young fellow, and for that reason my reprimand was that much less harsh; however, he did not forbear to lecture me because of what I had done. But just when the sermon was at its best and he asked me why I had thrashed my adversary so horribly, I answered: "Because he made a grab for my courage, which place no man's hands have touched." (For I wished to express myself delicately and did not wish to call it by as crude a name as the Suabians use for their penknives,[6] which, if I were master, would not be called such a vulgar word either, but would have to be called "naughty knives".) And because my virginity, all this notwithstanding, was breathing its last, particularly since I could not but hazard that my adversary would betray me anyway, look you, I bared my snow-white bosom and showed the captain of horse my firm, appealing breasts: "Look, sir!" I said, "Here you see before you a maiden who donned men's clothing in Prachatitz to save her honor from the soldiers; and since God and fortune have placed her in your

6. The German word to which Courage alludes is *Hegel* or *Hegi*, meaning bull or stud, also fool.

hands, she therefore beseeches you and hopes that you, as an honorable gentleman, will protect her and keep intact the honor which she has preserved." And after I had brought forth that, I began to weep so pitiably that one would have staked his life that everything I said was in dead earnest.

Although the captain of horse was greatly astounded, to be sure, he could not but laugh at how I had described with a new name many of the colors which were to be found on my escutcheon. He consoled me most kindly and promised with high-flown words to protect my honor like his own life; but with his deeds he soon showed that he would be the first to rob me of my maidenhead; and I myself liked his unchaste groping better than his honorable promises; however, I defended myself valiantly; not, of course, to escape him or to flee his lustful advances, but to really excite him and to make him even more lustful; and the trick succeeded so well in every way that I allowed nothing to happen till he promised, or might the devil fetch him, to wed me, despite the fact that I could well imagine that he had no more intention of keeping his promise than of cutting his own throat. And now, look you, my dear Simplex! You may have thought up till now that in Sauerbrunnen you were the first to skim the sweet cream off the top. Oh no, you booby, you were cheated, it was gone, perhaps even before you were born, wherefore, since you were tardy, you were justly entitled to and received nothing but the whey. But that is only child's play compared to the other ways I have led you on and cheated you, all of which you shall learn from me too, in its proper place.

Chapter 4

Courage becomes a married woman and wife of a captain of horse, solely because she must straightway become his widow, after she had lived the married life for a time, while being single

Thus I was now living in secret love with my captain of horse and serving him as both valet-de-chambre and wife. I often plagued him that he should at last keep his promise and lead me to the altar, but he always had an excuse for putting off the affair. I was never closer to bringing him to heel than when I professed my almost frantic love for him on the one hand and on the other bewailed like Jephthah's daughter [1] my lost virginity, which was really not worth a farthing to me; indeed, I was glad to be rid of such a heavy and intolerable burden, because now my curiosity had left me. However, with my charming importunity I did cajole him into getting me a striking dress in Vienna, in the latest style, as the noble ladies were then wearing them in Italy (so that I lacked nothing but the wedding ceremony and that they call me the captain's lady); and with this dress he raised my hopes and kept me willing. But I was not allowed to wear the dress nor admit that I was a woman, much less his spouse, and what vexed me most of all was that he henceforth no longer called me Janco, or even Libushka, but Courage. This name others imitated, without knowing its origin, but thinking that my master called me by it because it was my wont to expose myself to the greatest danger in the face of the enemy with my

1. *Jephthah's daughter*] Courage here is interpreting the Bible to suit her own ends. Actually, Jephthah's daughter went "and bewailed her virginity upon the mountains" (Judg. 11:38), but her lament was not that she has lost it, as Courage had, but that she must remain a virgin.

46

characteristic resolution and incomparable courage. Thus I had to swallow it, but it stuck in my craw.

Therefore, dear maidens who have kept your honor and your maidenhead inviolate, be warned and let them not be taken from you so carelessly, for with them your freedom goes down the river, and you end in such torture and slavery as is harder to endure than death itself; I speak from experience, and I could sing a song about that. The loss of my maidenhead, to be sure, did not grieve me, because I had never intended to buy a lock for it, but it did indeed pierce my heart that I should be forced to suffer ridicule because of it and, to top it all, give meek words in return, if I were not to live in fear that my captain of horse might tell tales out of school and expose me to the shame and mockery of all. And you fine fellows who play such highwaymen's tricks on women, take care that you do not receive the just reward for your wenching from her whom you have incited to take justified revenge, as for example happened in Paris[2] when a gentleman, having deceived a lady and then being about to marry another, was enticed to an assignation, then murdered by night, pitiably curtailed, and thrown out the window onto the street. For my part, I must confess that if my captain of horse had not entertained me with all manner of sincere protestations of love and had not kept me ever in the hope that in the end he would beyond any doubt wed me, I should have made him, during an engagement, the unexpected present of a musket-ball.

In the meantime, we marched into Hungary under General Bucquoy's command and first of all conquered Pressburg,[3] where we stored most of our baggage and best things, because my captain of horse foresaw that we should have to risk a pitched battle with Bethlen

2. *happened in Paris*] it is told in one of the *novelle* of Bandello: "Il Sig. Didaco Centiglia sposa una giovane, a poi non la vuole, e da lei e ammazato." The scene is Valencia.

3. *Pressburg*] May, 1622.

Gabor.[4] From there we went to St. Georgi, Bösen, Modern,[5] and other towns which were first plundered and then burned; we captured Tyrnau, Altenburg, and almost the entire island,[6] and we received a few blows from the enemy before Neusohl,[7] where my captain of horse was mortally wounded and also our general, Count Bucquoy was cut down, which death then caused us to take flight and not stop till we came to Pressburg. There I nursed my captain of horse with great diligence, but the surgeons prophesied him certain death, because he was wounded in the lung. Therefore he was enjoined and moved by good people to make his peace with God, for our regimental chaplain was such a zealous minister that he did not leave him in peace till he had confessed and taken communion. After that he was goaded and driven, both by his father confessor and by his own conscience, to take me to wife on his deathbed, which act was regarded as beneficial not so much for his body as for his soul; and this happened that much quicker because I persuaded him that I was with child by him. That shows how perverse things are in this world: Other men take wives to live with them till death do them part, but he took me to wife because he knew that death would soon us part!

From this chain of events people could not but believe that I had served him and was bewailing his sad fate not as a faithful servant but as his mistress. The dress which he had earlier gotten me served me well at the wedding ceremony, but I could not wear it long, but was obliged to have a black one, because in a few days he made me his widow; and at that time I felt like the woman who, at her husband's funeral, replied to a friend's condolences by saying: "The devil robs us first of what we love most." I had him buried splendidly enough,

4. *Bethlen Gabor*] Gabriel Bethlen, Prince of Transylvania (1580–1629), allied himself with the "Winter King" in 1619, invaded Hungary, and took Pressburg; crowned King of Hungary on August 25, 1620.

5. *St. Georgi, Bösen, Modern*] cities at the foot of the little Carpathians.

6. *island*] the island of Schuett below Pressburg.

7. *Neusohl*] a city near Kremnitz. Courage is in error here; the skirmish took place at Neuhaeusel on the river Neutra, July 10, 1621.

in accordance with his estate, for he left me not only beautiful horses, arms, and clothing, but also a good deal of money, and I had the priest give me a written document of all these events, in hopes of yet snatching something from the inheritance of his parents; but after diligent investigation I could learn only that he had indeed been of noble birth but, on the other hand, so poor that he should have been forced to scrape along miserably, if the Bohemians had not conveniently sent him or presented him with a war.

But in Pressburg I not only lost this, my beloved; I was also besieged by Bethlen Gabor in that same city. But when ten companies of horse and two regiments of foot succoured the city by a stratagem and Bethel despaired of victory and lifted the siege, I seized the first opportunity and betook myself to Vienna with my horses, servants, and all my baggage, with the idea in mind to go from there back to Bohemia, to see whether I might perhaps find my nurse still alive in Prachatitz and might learn from her who my parents had really been. At that time I flattered myself with not inconsiderable thoughts, namely about what honor and fame would surely be mine when I came back home and brought along so many horses and servants, all of which, as proven by my document, I had gotten fairly and squarely in the war.

Chapter 5

What a reputable and chaste, as well as infamous and godless life Courage, the wife of the captain of horse, led in widowhood, how she gives in to a count, deprives an ambassador of his pistoles, and yields to many others willingly, to snatch rich booty

Because I did not dare to undertake my planned journey from Vienna to Prachatitz so soon because of the troubled times, and particularly since it was deucedly expensive to eat at inns, I sold my horses and dismissed all my servants, and I hired instead a maid and rented from a widow a sitting room, bedroom, and kitchen, to live frugally and to wait for an opportunity to get home safely. This widow was a true trump-ace of harlotry, the likes of which was hard to find. Her two daughters, however, were of our ilk and well known to both courtiers and army officers, and they soon made me known to them also, so that these whoremongers were presently singing to one another the praises of the great beauty of the widow of the captain of horse who was staying with them. But just as my widow's weeds lent me a singular appearance and a reputable gravity, particularly since they made my beauty shine forth all the more, so I lived in the beginning very quiet and withdrawn.

My maid was obliged to spin while I applied myself to sewing, embroidery, and other such lady's work, making sure that people would see me at it, but secretly I pampered my beauty and could often stand for a whole hour in front of the mirror, to learn and comprehend how laughter, tears, sighs, and other such fleeting things became me; and this folly should have been sufficient indication to me of my frivolity and a certain prophecy that I should soon be imitating my landlady's daughters, who, to make sure that this might happen soon, began, together with the old woman, to cultivate my acquaintance; to amuse me they often visited me in my rooms, where then such discourse took place as is ordinarily quite unhealthy and not designed to preserve the innocence of such young things as I was then, particularly in such natures as are disposed like mine was. She knew how to achieve her ends most cleverly by devious by-ways and first of all taught my maid how to do my hair and dress me in the latest fashion. Me, however, she instructed how to make my white skin even whiter and my golden hair even more lustrous; and then, when she had groomed me this way, she would say that it was a pity that such a noble creature should forever be stuck in a black sack and should live like a mourning dove. Such flattery tamed me nicely and was oil on the already blazing fire of the compelling lusts within me. She also lent me *Amadis*[1] to pass the time with and to learn compliments from, and she did whatever else she could think of to incite my concupiscence.

In the meantime the servants whom I had dismissed had noised abroad and spread among the people what kind of a captain's wife I had been, and how I had come by that title; and because they knew not what else to call me I was once more left with the name "Courage." By and by I also began to forget my captain of horse, because he no longer kept me warm; and since I saw that my landlady's daughters were doing so well in their trade, my mouth gradually began to water for new meat, which my landlady was indeed more eager to serve me than herself. However, as long as I did not take off my widow's weeds she could not openly suggest such a thing to me, because she saw that I coldly rejected any insinuations in that direction. Nevertheless, several persons of rank did not forbear to inquire of her about me daily and to swarm round her house like wasps round a beehive.

Among them was a young count who had recently seen me in church and had fallen madly in love with me. He spent a great deal of money

1. *Amadis*] this romance of chivalry full of erotic love stories originated in Spain, became popular in France, appeared in German translation in 1583, and was one of the favorites of its time.

to secure access to me, and so that he might somehow achieve this end, since my landlady, whom he had approached in vain, did not as yet dare to brazenly bring him to me, he inquired of one of my former servants all the particulars concerning the regiment in which my husband had served; and when he knew the names of the officers he humbly asked permission to wait upon me, or to visit me personally, to inquire about his acquaintances, whom, of course, he had never in his life laid eyes on. From that he came to speak of my captain of horse, of whom he bragged that he had studied with him during his youth and had always enjoyed close acquaintance and familiarity with him; he also bemoaned his untimely death and thereby lamented at the same time my own misfortune, which had so soon made me a widow at such a tender age, with the offer that if I should in any matter be in need of his help, &c. With this and similar gambits the young gentleman sought to make his first acquaintance with me, which indeed he did; and even though I well understood that he was unfamiliar with the truth (for my captain of horse had really never studied at all), I nevertheless was pleased by his manner, because he was bent on taking the place of my departed captain of horse. But I acted very cold and remote, gave curt answers, pressed forth some pretty tears, and thanked him for his compassion and proffered kindness with such compliments as were designed to indicate to him sufficiently that for now his love must be satisfied with a good beginning, but that he ought nevertheless take honorable leave of me now.

The next day he sent his lackey to learn if he would discommode me if he came to visit me. I sent back word that he would not actually discommode me and that I even enjoyed his company, but because there were peculiar people in this world to whom everything appeared suspicious, I begged him to spare me and not to bring me into ill repute. This unmannerly reply not only did not make the count angry, it made him that much more amorous; mule-in-cholic-ly,[2] he walked past my

---

2. *mule-in-cholicly*] the German is *maulhenkolisch*, a word play which fuses *melancholisch* (melancholic) with *maulhängerisch* (down-in-the-mouth).

2. Peasant Beating His Donkey. 1628

house in hopes of at least feasting his eyes, should he perhaps see me at
the window, but in vain: I was anxious to sell my wares as dearly as
possible and kept out of sight. Now when he was half dying of love I
took off my widow's weeds and decked myself out in my other dress,
in which I could indeed make a show; I did everything that might
adorn my person and thereby drew the eyes and hearts of many
eminent persons upon myself, which happened, however, only when
I went to church, because I never went anywhere else. Every day there
were greetings and messages for me from this one and that one who
lay sick with the same distemper as the count; but I remained as
unyielding as a rock, till all Vienna was filled not only with praise for
my incomparable beauty but also with the fame of my chastity and
other rare virtues.

Now when I had brought it to such a point that everyone very
nearly took me to be half a saint, I thought it time for once to give full
rein to the lusts I had hitherto held in check and to deceive the people
in their good opinion of me. The count was the first whom I promised
and granted my favors, because he had spared neither effort nor expense
to gain them. Though he was, to be sure, worthy of love and loved me
with all his heart, and though I took him to be the best of the lot to
satisfy my lusts, he still would not have succeeded if he had not sent me,
right after I took off my widow's weeds, a piece of dove-colored satin
with all the trimmings for a new dress and, more important, if he had
not presented me with a hundred ducats for my household, so that I
might the better console myself for the loss of my husband. The next
one after him was the ambassador of a great potentate who the first
night made me earn sixty pistoles;[3] after him there were others too,
and none, to be sure, who could not spend boldly; for anyone who
was poor, or at least not very rich and high in rank, could either stay
away or make do with my landlady's daughters. And in this manner
I managed it so that my mill, as it were, never stood idle; and it ground

3. *pistoles*] the word play with coins and "pistols" in the subtitle of this chapter
is not as evident in English.

away so well that within a month I raked in more than a thousand ducats in specie, not counting the other things given to me, such as jewelry, rings, necklaces, bracelets, velvet, silk and linen (no one dared to present me with mere stockings or gloves), also victuals, wines, and other things; and I thought to make use of my youth henceforth in this way, because I knew the old saw:

> Each day from beauty steals his share,
> Till Charon asks the final fare.

And I should regret it to this very day if I had done less. Finally it got so bad that people began to point their fingers at me, and I could well imagine that in the long run things would come to a bad end; for finally I was not even refusing lesser folk a ride. My landlady assisted me faithfully and also made her honest profit from it. She taught me all kinds of fine tricks, not just those which women of easy virtue know, but also those which men without honor resort to at times, even how to make myself shotfree[4] and how to close by magic any man's gun, if I wished to, and I believe that if I had stayed longer with her I should even have learned witchcraft too. But since I was reliably warned that the magistrate intended to take us out of our nest and destroy it, I bought a light carriage and two horses, hired a manservant, and with them, but without warning, I shook the dust from my heels, for I happened to have a good opportunity to get safely to Prague.

4. *shotfree*] the old belief that by sorcery it was possible to make oneself invulnerable.

Chapter 6

Courage, through a wondrous turn of fate, enters into marriage a second time and weds a captain of infantry, with whom she lives in great happiness and joy

I should have had an excellent opportunity in Prague to ply my trade further; but the desire to see my nurse and to inquire about my parents drove me to travel to Prachatitz, which, since it was through country at peace, I thought to be safe; but Amor take me, when, one evening, I could already see the town lying before me, eleven of Mansfeld's [1] troopers happened by whom I, as everyone else had done, took to be Imperial troops and therefore friends, because they were wearing red sashes or insignia. They seized me and traveled off with me and my carriage in the direction of the Bohemian Forest as if the devil himself were chasing them. Of course, I screamed as if I were stretched on the rack, but they soon silenced me. At midnight they came to a farm which lay by itself at the edge of the forest where they began to feed the horses and to do with me what is generally done on such occasions, which was, I confess, the least of my worries; but it profited them like grass does a dog: For while they were gratifying their bestial lusts they were fallen upon by a captain of infantry with thirty dragoons [2] who had been on convoy duty to Pilsen, and because

1. *Mansfeld*] Count Ernest von Mansfeld (1580–1626), an officer in Archduke Leopold's army until real or fancied ingratitude of his prince drove him into the arms of the Habsburg enemies. He remained a Catholic until he allied himself with the Protestant princes and became one of their foremost champions.

2. *dragoons*] mounted infantrymen who took their name from their weapon, a species of carbine, or short musket, called the "dragon." Their officers bore infantry titles.

they had denied their rightful master by their false insignia, every man jack of them was cut down.

Mansfeld's troopers had not yet divided my possessions, and since I had an Imperial pass and had not yet been in enemy hands for twenty-four hours, I represented to the captain of infantry that he could take neither me nor my possessions for or as legitimate booty. This he himself was obliged to admit, but, he said, I was nevertheless indebted to him for my deliverance, nor could he be blamed if he did not intend to let such a treasure as he had taken from the enemy slip through his fingers; whereas I was the widow of a captain of horse, he said, he was a widower captain of infantry. If I were willing, the booty should soon be divided; if not, then he would take me along anyway and afterwards dispute with anyone whether the booty was rightfully his or not. With this he showed sufficiently that I had already turned his head; and that he might have grist for his mill, he said, he would leave me this advantage: That I might choose whether he should divide the booty among all his men or whether I and what belonged to me should be his alone through marriage, in which case he was sure he could convince the men with him that I and mine were not legitimate booty, but belonged to him alone because he had married me. I answered that if I had any choice I desired neither, but rather it was my request that they let me pass in my own custody; and with that I began to weep as if I were in dead earnest, as the old rhyme says:

> Women weep with moans and sighs,
> But see! Their tears are only lies,
> For they but feign that they fare ill:
> Women can weep whene'er they will.

But it was my intention in doing this to give him good reason to console me and to become even more enamored of me, since I well knew that men's hearts generally open most readily to a lady in tears and distress. The trick succeeded too, and as he was appealing to me and assuring me of his love with high-flown words, I consented to marry him, but with the express condition and proviso that he should not touch my person at all till after the ceremony, which promise he both made and kept, till we arrived in the Mansfeld fortifications at Weidhausen,[3] which at just that time were being surrendered *per accord* by Mansfeld himself to the Duke of Bavaria. And because my *serviteur's* fervent love could brook no delay of our wedding, we were joined in wedlock before he could find out how Courage had earned her money, which was no small sum.

I had hardly been with the army for a month when I met several high-ranking officers who had not only known me in Vienna but had also been good customers of mine; but they were so discreet that they proclaimed neither my dishonor nor their own. To be sure, a tiny whisper went about, but nevertheless I was not particularly annoyed by it, except that I had to put up with the name "Courage" once more.

Otherwise I had a good, patient husband who was just as pleased with my yellow coin as he was with my beauty. He was a bit more thrifty with them than I liked; but since I bore with him in this, he, for his part, allowed me to be that much more liberal in speech and bearing toward everyone. When someone then teased him that he might in time be presented with horns, he in turn answered jokingly that that was the least of his worries; for even if someone might succeed with his wife, he would not leave it at that, but rather take the time to set aright such unfamiliar work. He always kept an excellent horse for me, mounted with a beautiful saddle and tack; I did not ride in a lady's saddle like other officers' ladies, but instead in a man's saddle, and though I rode sidesaddle I still had pistols and a Turkish sabre under my thigh and always left a stirrup hanging free on the off-side, and moreover I was dressed in breeches and a thin little taffeta skirt over them, so that in an instant I could sit astride and present the picture of a young trooper; for if there was an encounter with the enemy it was impossible for me to stay off to the side and not take part. I often said

3. *Weidhausen*] a village in the Upper Palatinate where Mansfeld had a fortified camp.

that a lady who does not dare defend herself against a mounted man ought not to wear man's plumage; and after I had the good fortune at a few of these bouts to take prisoners who did not think themselves sluggards, I became so bold when there were such skirmishes as to also hang a carbine, or bandoleer-musket, as they call them, on my saddle and was ready to fight two at a time while separated from my own troop, and that all the more boldly because through the trick which I had learned from my oft-mentioned landlady I and my horse were so shotfree that no musket-ball could harm me.

So it went and so it was with me at that time; I took more booty than many a sworn soldier, which indeed angered many; but I paid little heed to that, for it was butter on my bread. The trust placed in me by my husband, who (compared to me, at least) was not very well equipped, caused me to remain true to his colors, even though higher ranks than captains reported to me to take his place as his *lieu-tenant*;[4] for he allowed me great freedom in many respects. On the other hand and all this notwithstanding, I was merry in company, brazen in conversation, but also as heroic as any man against the enemy, in the field as thrifty and frugal as any housewife, in the care of the horses better than any equerry, and in garrison of such prosperity that my captain of infantry could not have wished for better; and when he had cause to rebuke me at times, he was quite willing that I contradict him and act on my own judgment, because our money multiplied as a result to such an extent that we were obliged to put a good part of it into safekeeping in a large city. And so I lived in great happiness and joy and should never in my life have wished for any other trade, if only my husband had been a little bit better in the saddle. But my *fatum* or fortune did not leave me long in this state, for after my captain of infantry was shot to death at Wiesloch,[5] look you, I suddenly became a widow once more.

4. *lieu-tenant*] the German is a word play on *stellvertreten* (take the place of) and the original meaning of the French word *lieutenant* (taking the place of).

5. *Wiesloch*] in Baden, where Mansfeld defeated the Bavarian forces in 1622.

Chapter 7

Courage enters into marriage a third time, and instead of being the wife of a captain of infantry becomes the wife of a lieutenant, but does not score as well as before, fights with cudgels against her husband for his trousers, winning same through her brave resolution and courage, whereupon her husband vanishes, jilting her

My husband was hardly cold in his grave when I again had a dozen suitors from among whom I could choose, for I was not only young and beautiful, but also had handsome horses and a great deal of good money, and though I had it noised abroad that for the sake of my late captain of infantry I intended to observe mourning for half a year at least, I nevertheless could not drive off the importunate bumblebees that were buzzing about me as around a fat honeypot without a lid. The colonel promised me victuals and quarters with the regiment till I had made other arrangements. I, in turn, had two of my manservants serve with the army, and when there was an occasion at which I was confident to snatch some booty from the enemy, I spared my hide no more than any soldier, as witness how I captured a lieutenant in the pleasant, almost merry battle of Wimpfen[1] and in harrassing the rear guard not far from Heilbronn,[2] a cornet together with his standard;[3] at the

1. *Wimpfen*] where Count Johann Tzerclaes von Tilly (1599–1632), general of the army of the Catholic League, defeated the Margrave of Baden, May 6, 1622.
2. *Heilbronn*] a city on the Neckar River.
3. *cornet together with his standard*] the fifth-ranking commissioned officer in a cavalry troop in seventeenth-century armies, the cornet had the duty of carrying the standard into battle. The capture of a company's standard was more significant at this period than in later times, for more than the honor of the unit was at stake. C. V. Wedgewood notes: "The soldiers [of the mercenary armies] once enlisted were faithful only to their banners. The oath which they took was not to any personal leader of State but to the flag, and if the flag were captured in battle the

plundering of the wagons my two servants took a great deal of booty in cash money, which they were obliged to divide with me, according to our agreement.

After this battle I had more lovers than before, and since I had had with my former husband more good days than nights, and particularly since I had been fasting against my will since his death, look you, so I thought to make up by my choice for all that I had missed and promised to marry a lieutenant who to my mind outstripped all his rivals in beauty, youth, intelligence, and bravery. He was an Italian by birth and of course black of hair, but fair of skin, and to my eyes so handsome that no painter could have painted him any handsomer. He showed towards me almost a doglike humility till he had courted and won me, and when he had my consent he acted as joyful as if God had condemned the whole world and saved his soul alone. We were married in the Palatinate and had the honor of having the colonel himself, along with most of the high-ranking officers of the regiment, in attendance at our wedding, all of whom wished us much happiness in a long life together, but, alas, in vain.

For at sunrise after the first night, as we were lying together, idling away the time and entertaining one another with all manner of dallying and friendly conversation, just as I myself was about to rise, my lieutenant called his page to the bed and commanded him to bring two stout cudgels. He obeyed, and I, imagining the poor rogue would needs be the first to test their worth, did not therefore forbear to intercede for the lad, till he had brought both cudgels and, following orders, laid them on the table with the nightclothes. Now when the boy had left us once more, my bridegroom said to me: "Now, darling, you know that everyone supposed and believed that you wore the trousers while your former husband was yet alive, which was reported of him in fine society to his not inconsiderable disgrace; because I, not unjustly, have cause to fear that you might persist in this habit and

soldiers were at liberty to follow it" (*The Thirty Years War* [New Haven: Yale University Press, 1939], p. 87).

might wish to wear mine too, which to suffer I, however, would find impossible, or at least difficult, look you, there on the table are my trousers and with them those two cudgels, so that you and I may first fight for the trousers,[4] in case you perhaps indeed intend to claim them or confer them unto yourself, as you did with him, since my love can herself appreciate that it would be better if they straightway in the beginning fell to one or the other party than that we hereafter should daily wage war for the right to wear them."

I answered: "My darling" (and herewith I gave him a very hearty kiss), "I should have thought that the kind of battle in which we should engage at a time like this had already been fought; also, it never entered my mind to pretend to your trousers; rather, just as I well know that woman was taken not from man's head but indeed from his side, I had hoped likewise that this was known to my heart's dearest as well and that he would therefore remember my origin and regard me as his mate and not his doormat, as if I had been scraped off the soles of his feet, particularly since I for my part did not presume to sit on his head, but would be content to sit at his side, with the humble plea that he might call a halt to this outlandish fencing match."

"Hah!" he said, "those are truly womanly wiles to seize authority before a man be aware of it; but first of all the trousers must be fought for, so that I may know who in the future shall owe obedience to whom." And with that he tore himself from my arms like that other fool.[5]

I, for my part, sprang out of bed and put on my shirt and drawers, snatched up the shortest but stoutest cudgel, and said: "Because you have commanded me to fight and have ceded to the victor sovereignty over the vanquished (to which sovereignty, after all, I had no desire to lay claim), I should be a fool indeed if I let slip through my fingers an

---

4. *fight for the trousers*] a similar episode is to be found in the spurious Moscherosch continuation of 1648 in which a bridegroom threatens his bride with a sword and gets her to promise to be faithful to the death.

5. *that other fool*] an allusion to Simplicissimus, who also spurned her.

opportunity to gain something which I should otherwise not have dared think of."

He, for his part, also not idle, while I was waiting for him thus, after he too had put on his trousers, seized the other cudgel and thought to grasp me by the hair in order to thoroughly belabor my backside at his leisure. But I was much too quick for him, for before he knew it, he had a rap on the head from which he went down like a poleaxed bull. I gathered up the two staffs to throw them out of the door, and when I opened it, there, outside, stood several officers who had listened to our dispute and in part watched through a crack in the door; these I let laugh as long as they liked, clapped the door to in their faces, put on my gown, brought my booby—I mean my bridegroom—back to his senses with water from the wash basin; and when I had set him at the table and gotten partly dressed, let the officers outside come in.

How we all looked at each other, anyone may well imagine. I well remarked that my bridegroom had caused these officers to stand outside our room at this hour and be witnesses to his folly; for when they had teased my stud,[6] saying that he must needs let me wear the trousers, he had bragged to them that he had a singular plan which he would put to work that first morning and by which he would make me so docile that I would tremble if he but looked at me askance; but the good man should have tried it on someone other than Courage. Against me he merely accomplished that he became an object of ridicule to all, and I should not even have kept him in the house if I had not been commanded and enjoined to do so by his superiors; how we got along together, anyone can easily imagine, namely like cat and dog. Now when he could not avenge himself on me in any other way and could bear the public mockery no longer, he collected all my cash money and with three of my best horses and one of my servants went over to the enemy.

6. *stud*] here the German has the word *Hegel* mentioned in Chapter 3, note 5.

Chapter 8

Courage acts most courageously sharp during an engagement, hacks off a soldier's head, takes a major prisoner, and finds out that her lieutenant has been caught and hanged as a disloyal turncoat

Thus I now became a half-widow, which is far more miserable than having no husband at all. Some suspected that I would follow him and that we had planned our flight this way together; but when I asked the colonel for advice and orders as to how to act, he said I might stay with the regiment and he would have me provided for like other widows, as long as I behaved reputably; and with that I set to rest the above-mentioned suspicions of all and sundry. I was obliged to pull in my belt, since my cash had fled, and my magnificent cavalry horses, on which I had taken much magnificent booty, were gone; but I hid my poverty so that I should not become an object of contempt. I still had my two manservants, who were doing forced service with the army, together with a boy and several jades, or baggage horses; of these and of my men's baggage I turned what could be sold into silver and equipped myself again with an excellent mount.

Of course, as a woman I was not allowed to ride on any patrols, but there was none equal to me among the foragers. I often wished for another battle like the one before Wimpfen; but to what avail? I was obliged to bide my time, because they would not fight a battle just to please me, even if I had demanded it. But that I might somehow again come by some money, which was seldom found on foraging parties, I (both to earn money and to repay my runaway for his faithlessness) let whoever spent lavishly engage me; and in this way I got along and even hired as a servant a strong boy who was obliged to help me steal while the other two stood watch.

I continued in this manner till we chased the Prince of Brunswick[1] across the river Main and drowned many of his men in it, during which engagement I mingled with our troops and so distinguished myself in the presence of my colonel that he would not have believed such bravery of any man; for in the tumult I carried off a major from the other side, right in front of his troops, while he was trying to mount another attack; and when one of his own side thought to save him and to this end fired off his pistol at my head, blowing off my hat and plume, I repaid him in such fashion with my sabre that he rode along beside me for a few paces without any head at all, which was both wondrous and loathsome to behold. Now after this same cavalry squadron had been separated and put to flight, and after the major had given me, to spare his life, a considerable pile of all kinds of gold coin, a golden chain, and a valuable ring, I had my boy change horses with him and turned him over to our troops for safekeeping.

Thereupon I betook myself to the destroyed bridge, where in the water a miserable drowning and on land a cruel massacre was taking place; and since at this point everyone else was still obliged to stay with his own unit, as far as possible, I snatched six handsome bays and a carriage in which there was neither money nor any living soul, but two chests of costly clothes and white linen. I brought it, with the help of my servant, or boy, to the place where I had left the major, who was nearly vexed to death that he had been taken prisoner by such a young woman; but when he saw pistols sticking in the pockets of my breeches as well as in my holsters, which arms I was reloading and readying there, together with my carbine, and when he also heard what I had earlier accomplished at Wimpfen, he became somewhat less grieved and said that the devil himself might deal with such a witch. I went with my boy (whom I had made as shotfree as myself and my horse) to snatch still more booty, but instead found there, pinned under his horse, the lieutenant colonel of our regiment, who knew me and cried

1. *Prince of Brunswick*] Prince Christian of Brunswick, Administrator of the secularized bishopric of Halberstadt, who was defeated in the battle of Höchst, a town on the Main east of Frankfurt, by Tilly on June 20, 1622.

to me for help. I packed him onto my boy's horse and took him to our side to my captured wagon, in which he had to suffer my captured major's company.

One can hardly believe how I was praised after this battle, both by those who envied and those who favored me; both said that I was the devil himself; and at just that time it was my most fervent wish not to be a woman; but what help was that? It had been bungled from the start. I often thought of pretending to be a hermaphrodite, to see whether this way I might gain the right to wear trousers in public and pass for a young fellow; but on the other hand, because of my incontinent lusts I had made so many men sensible of my sex that I did not have the gall to do what I should have liked to do; for so many witnesses would have said differently of me and would have caused it to come to the point where both *medici* and midwives would needs have examined me; therefore I got along as best I could, and when I was criticized, I answered that in former times there had been, after all, Amazons who had fought against the enemy as valiantly as any man. So as to keep in the good graces of my colonel and to be protected by him from those who wished me ill, I presented him with both my prisoner and my carriage, together with the horses, for which he gave me two hundred sovereigns, which money I again put into safekeeping in a large city, together with what else I had recently snatched or otherwise earned.

Now after we had captured Mannheim[2] and were still laying siege to Frankenthal[3] and were therefore playing the overlord in the Palatinate, look you, then Cordoba and von Anhalt[4] once more defeated the Prince of Brunswick and the Duke of Mansfeld at Fleurus,[5] in which encounter my runaway husband, the lieutenant, was captured

2. *Mannheim*] taken on October 23, 1622.

3. *Frankenthal*] besieged since September 19, 1622.

4. *Cordoba and von Anhalt*] Gonzales de Cordoba, general of the Spanish troops; Johann Jacob Count of Anhalt, died 1630.

5. *Fleurus*] Fleurus or Fleury (Latin: Floriacum), a town in the county of Namur where Mansfeld and the Duke of Brunswick defeated Cordoba on August 29, 1622.

and recognized by our side, and, being a disloyal turncoat, was hanged from a tree by his fine neck; by this I was freed once more from my husband and made a widow, to be sure, but I also made such a lot of enemies, who said: "That blasted witch cost the poor devil his life" that I would have gladly granted him a little longer life and put up with him a while longer, till he bit the dust somewhere else and found a more honorable death, if only that had been possible.

Chapter 9

Courage quits the war since her star is beginning to set and she is being held up to ridicule by almost everyone

So it happened by and by that the longer I stayed there the more I had to endure: My servants were led astray because they were told: "How the devil can you men serve such a slut?" I hoped to get another husband, but everyone said: "You take her, I don't want her!" Whoever was reputable shook his head at me, and so did almost all of the officers too; and common folk or petty potentates were not allowed to approach me; I should not have deigned to look at any of them anyway. To be sure, I did not get a pain in the neck from our foolish duel like my husband did; but I suffered longer because of it than he did when they hanged him. I should have liked to slip on a different skin, but neither habit nor my daily society would allow me any improvement, just as most people grow worse rather than better in times of war. I dressed up again to trap or to snare the one or the other, to see whether I might not entice this one or that one into my net; but nothing helped: I had indeed already fallen much too much into ill repute; Courage was certainly well known throughout the entire army, and whenever I rode past the regiments my honor was loudly proclaimed by many thousands of voices, so that very nearly like a night owl I no longer dared to show my face by day. On the march reputable women avoided me; the ragtag rabble with the baggage train baited me the rest of the time; and whatever single officers might have protected me in return for a night's grazing in my pasture were obliged to stay with their regiments, where, however, because of all the disgraceful clamor, I was being raked over the coals, so that I clearly saw that in the long run things would come to a bad end. A few officers were still my friends, but they were out for their own advantage and not mine; some sought gratification of their own lust, some my money, others my handsome horses; but all of them meant trouble for me, the parasites, and yet not one of them wished to marry me, either because they were ashamed to, or because they ascribed to me some unlucky faculty which was supposed to be harmful to anyone who was my husband, or even because, I know not why, they were somehow afraid of me.

Therefore I decided to quit not only this regiment but also the army, in fact the whole war, and I could accomplish this the more easily because the high-ranking officers would have liked to be rid of me long ago; indeed, I cannot be persuaded either to believe that there were many among the reputable people who shed many tears at my departure, except perhaps a few unmarried dandies among the officers of lower rank for whom I at some time or other had washed a few drawers. The colonel did not like to hear it told how his beautiful carriage had been taken from the enemy and presented to him by Courage. That I had saved the wounded lieutenant colonel from the battle and the danger of death and led him safely to our side, he considered such slight honor to himself that he not only thanked me for my trouble by wishing the plague on me, but blushed with a hangdog look when he saw me and, as is easy to imagine, wished me nothing less than health and good fortune. The ladies, or officers' wives, hated me because I was far more beautiful than any other in the entire regiment, and particularly because I pleased some of the husbands better than they did themselves; and both noncommissioned officers and soldiers were hostile toward me because more than any one of them I had the heart to undertake and accomplish things which demanded the utmost bravery and boldest daring, things which would have given anyone else goose pimples.

Now since I easily remarked that I had many more foes than friends, I could also well imagine that any of my backbiting ilk would not forbear to play me a trick of their particular kind, should only the opportunity arise. "Oh, Courage!" I said to myself, "how will you be able to escape so many different enemies, of whom perhaps each one has in mind his own particular plot against you? If you had nothing but your beautiful horses, your beautiful dresses, your beautiful arms, and the reputation of having much money on your person, there would be enemies enough to incite some scoundrel to assassinate you secretly. What if such a rascal were to murder you or cut you down during an engagement? Who would give a hoot about it? Who would avenge your death? Why? Ought you dare even trust your own servants?" With such worries I tortured myself and also asked myself what to do, because I did not have anyone else who was my true friend; and just because of this I had to follow my own counsel.

Accordingly, I appealed to the colonel for a pass to the closest Imperial city, which was just at hand and was well located to put some distance between me and the troops; I not only got it with little trouble, but even got instead of a discharge a document which attested that I had been respectably married to a captain of infantry of the regiment (for of my last husband I had no desire to brag), and that when I had lost him in battle I had remained for a time with the regiment, that during this time I had conducted myself well, gently, and reputably, as is seemly and befits a decent woman who loves her honor and virtue, and that therefore I should be highly recommended to one and all for my blamelessly virtuous conduct. And such fat lies were confirmed in the most proper manner by a handwritten signature and an affixed seal. And let no one wonder at this, for the worse a body conducts himself, and the more one would like to be rid of him, the more excellent will be the farewell with which he will be sped on his way, particularly if it must also serve as his wages. To show my gratitude I left with the colonel's company a horse and a servant who, though he was not an officer, was nevertheless well mounted; but I myself escaped with a servant, a boy, a maid, six beautiful horses (every one of which was worth a hundred ducats), together with a well-lined wagon. And I cannot say in good conscience (some call it bad conscience) with which hand I captured and acquired all these things.

Now after I had brought myself and all my possessions into safety in the above-mentioned city, I turned my horses into silver and rid myself of everything else which was worth hard cash and which I did not actually need; I also dismissed all of my servants to spare expenses. But the same thing that had happened to me in Vienna happened to me here again: I could not rid myself of the name "Courage," even though of all I owned I should have let it go most cheaply, for my old, or rather, my young customers from the army rode into town on my account and inquired after me by this name, which the children in the streets learned before they did the *Pater noster*, and for this very reason I showed my gallants the fig.[1] But when, on the other hand, they told the city folk what a trump-ace harlot I was, I, for my part, proved differently to them with my signed and sealed document and persuaded them that the officers were telling such lewd tales about me for the sole reason that I lacked those talents which they would like to ascribe to me. And in this manner I fairly bluffed my way through, and by means of my good written testimonial I brought it to pass that the city lent me its protection on payment of a small fee of succor, till I should have the opportunity to travel elsewhere; here, against my will, I behaved most reputably, gently, quietly, and withdrawn, and tended most assiduously to my beauty, which increased with each passing day, in the hopes of getting, in time, a good husband once more.

1. *fig*] "showed them my nose." The German reads "wiese meinen Galanen die Feigen" (showed my gallants the fig); the fig, or fica, was a widely current obscene gesture.

Chapter 10

Courage learns who her parents were and gets yet another husband

But I should have been obliged to wait a long time till I got a good bite, for the good families associated only with one another, and whoever else was rich could also choose a wife from among maidens who were rich, beautiful, and, above all, virtuous too (which in those times still counted for something), so that they had no need to tangle with an abandoned soldiers' whore. On the other hand, there were some who were either bankrupt or about to be; they desired my money, to be sure, but therefore I did not desire them; tradesmen were of course too much beneath me, and so I stayed single for an entire year, which was hard for me to tolerate longer and completely against my nature, particularly since I began to itch more and more as a result of the good life I was leading; for I used the money which I kept here and there in large cities to loan to bankers and merchants from time to time, from which I made such an honest little profit that I was able to live pretty well from it and was not obliged to touch the principal at all. But because I was suffering want in another place and my weak legs either could not or would not bear this much of a good thing any longer, I sent my money to Prague per bill of exchange, following myself in the company of some merchants, and sought refuge with my old nurse in Prachatitz, to see whether perhaps a better fortune might await me there.

I found her much poorer than I had left her; for not only had the war played ill with her, but even before the war she had lived off me and not I off her. She rejoiced greatly at my arrival, particularly when she saw that I had not wandered in empty-handed. Nevertheless, her first greeting was nothing but sobs, and while she was kissing me she called me an unfortunate young lady who would hardly be able to live in the manner to which her birth entitled her, with the further statement that she would not be able to further aid, counsel, and assist me as she had done earlier, because my best friends and relatives were either exiled or even dead; and moreover, she said, I should hardly be able to show my face on the Imperial side if they were to know of my origin. And with that she continued to wail so that I could make neither head nor tail of what she said, nor comprehend whether it was a matter of joking or croaking, sticks or stones.

But once I had restored her with food and drink (for the poor ninny had been forced to pull in her belt considerably) and thereby had so refreshed her that she was nearly tipsy, she told me candidly about my origin and said that my natural father had been a count[1] and only a few years ago the most powerful lord in the whole realm, but had now been exiled because he had rebelled against the Emperor and, as was being noised abroad, was now in Turkey, where he was also said to have even exchanged his Christian faith for the Turkish religion. My mother, she said, though of an honorable family, had been as poor as she was beautiful; she had been maid of honor at the court of said count's wife, and while she was serving the countess, the count himself became her servant and had indeed performed such services that after he had brought her to a country estate she was delivered of me; and because at that very time my nurse was weaning a young son, whom she had begot with the lord of that same manor, she had been obliged to become my wet nurse and later to bring me up as a noblewoman in Prachatitz, for which both father and mother had provided sufficient

---

1. *my natural father . . . a count*] there has been much conjecture about the identity of the person whom Grimmelshausen has in mind (later referred to as "Count of T—"). He was probably Count Heinrich Matthias of Thurn, who in October, 1622, was condemned by the Emperor and fled to Constantinople. It is also possible that Grimmelshausen meant Count Ernst von Mansfeld, who was banished in 1618; he was serving with Bethlen Gabor at the time Courage was taken by the Swedes, and there was a rumor that he had renounced Christianity in favor of the Moslem faith (Islam).

3. The Battle. From *The Miseries and Disasters of War*. 1633

means and sustenance. "It is true, dear Mistress," she said further, "that you were promised by your father to a valiant nobleman; but he was taken prisoner during the conquest of Pilsen and hanged as a traitor with several others by the Imperial side."

Thus I found out what I had long since wished to know and now wished that I had never found it out, particularly since I could hope for so little gain from my noble birth; and because I knew no other or better counsel, I made a pact with my nurse that henceforth she was to act as my mother and I as her daughter. She was much craftier than I, wherefore at her advice I moved from Prachatitz to Prague, not only to get out of sight of acquaintances but also to see whether perhaps a better fortune might not smile on us there. For the rest, we were just right for one another. Not that she should have acted the bawd and I the whore, but rather because she needed a breadwinner and I needed a faithful person (just like her) to whom I could entrust both my reputation and my property. Besides clothes and jewelry, I had almost three thousand sovereigns in cash and therefore, at that time, no cause to earn my bread by disgraceful means. My mother I dressed like a reputable old matron, held her in high esteem, and showed her every courtesy when other people were about; we claimed to be people who had been driven from the German border by the war, sought our livelihood by sewing and also by gold and silver embroidery on silk, and for the rest conducted ourselves very quietly and withdrawn, saving my pennies, since they are apt to melt away before one knows it, and one cannot simply earn more of them whenever one would like to.

Now this would have been a fine life which we led, indeed one might say a cloistered life, as it were, if only we had not lacked constancy. I soon found paramours; some sought me like a trollop in a bordello, and other boobies, who did not dare pay me for my honor, talked to me much of marriage; both parties, however, wished to persuade me that they were spurred on in their lusts by the terrible love they bore me. I should not have believed either of them, even if I had had a chaste bone in my whole body; it went according to the old saw: Like will to like; for just as they say: Straw in the shoes, a spindle in the pocket, and a whore in the house cannot be hidden.

So I was soon known and famous everywhere too because of my beauty; because of this, we received much to knit, and among other things a swordbelt for a captain of infantry who claimed he was breathing his last for love of me. On the other hand, I was able to brag so about my chastity that he acted as if he were going to despair completely; for I measured the character and wealth of my customers according to the rule of mine host, the innkeeper of the Golden Lion at N——. He said: "If a guest comes to me and pays me far too many compliments, it is a sure sign that he either does not intend to order the best or intends to spend little; but if someone is surly and takes lodgings with me with demands and lordly domineering ways, as it were, then I think: Hello! This fellow is suffering from a swollen purse which must be lanced. So I treat the polite ones politely, so that they may praise me and my inn elsewhere, but the complainers I give everything they desire, so that I may have good reason to properly cut their purses."

While I treated my captain of infantry like the innkeeper treated his polite guests, he, in like manner, took me to be, if not an angel, then at least the model and image of Chastity, in fact Virtue herself. *In summa*, he went so far as to begin talking to me of marriage and kept on till he had received my consent. The articles of the marriage contract were as follows: I was to bring him a thousand sovereigns in cash, but he, for his part, was to insure for me in his homeland in Germany that same amount, so that if he should die before me without heirs I could get them back; the other two thousand sovereigns which I had left were to be put out at interest in a safe place, and the interest was to be used by my husband during this marriage, but the principal was to remain untouched till we had heirs; also, I was to have power, if I should die without heirs, to leave my entire estate, including the thousand sovereigns which I had brought to him, to anybody I wished, &c.

Accordingly, the wedding was held; and while we were thinking that for as long as the war lasted we should live quietly together in the garrison in Prague, look you, orders arrived that we must march to Holstein to take part in the Danish campaign.

Chapter 11

After Courage begins to lead an upright life she unexpectedly becomes a widow again

I fitted myself out excellently for the campaign, because I really knew better than my captain of infantry what was needed; and because I feared having to go back where they were acquainted with Courage, I told my husband of my entire life, except for the whore's capers which I had undertaken here and there and except for what had happened between me and the captain of horse; concerning the name "Courage," I persuaded him that I had acquired it because of my bravery, which is what everyone believed anyway. By telling him this I anticipated those who otherwise might have blackened my name, should they have told him this and even more, indeed more than I should have liked. And just as he at first hardly believed how I had conducted myself in open battle against the enemy till others with the army later testified to the truth of it, so afterwards he did not believe other people who bragged to him of my evil doings, because I denied them. Except for falling into this trap he was very prudent and reasonable in all his actions, handsome in appearance, and one of those stouthearted men, so that I often wondered myself why he had taken me, since he more rightfully deserved a decent woman.

My mother I took with me as a housekeeper and cook, because she did not wish to stay behind. I equipped our baggage wagon with everything which one could possibly need in the field and made such a fuss among the servants that my husband had neither to worry himself, nor did he need a steward; myself, however, I equipped as before with a horse, arms, saddle and tack, and thus furnished we came upon Tilly's troops near the two fortresses called Gleichen,[1] where I was soon recognized and acclaimed by a crowd of cavilers "Cheer up, fellows! We have a good omen for winning future battles!"

"Why?"

"Because we have gotten our Courage back again!"

And as a matter of fact, these clowns were not far from the truth, for the troops with whom I arrived were reinforcements of three regiments of horse and two of foot, which was nothing to scoff at but enough to give the army courage even if I had not been there myself.

As far as I can recall, my own troop exchanged blows with the King of Denmark at Lutter[2] on the second day after this fortunate conjunction, at which engagement I certainly did not intend to remain with the baggage train, but instead, after the enemy's first ardor had cooled somewhat and our side had bravely renewed the fighting, I plunged into the midst of the press where the fighting was the thickest. I did not wish to take any mean scoundrel prisoner, but wished to show my husband straightway from the start that my nickname was fitting indeed, nor need he be ashamed of it; therefore I made room with my sabre for my noble stallion, the likes of which was not to be found in Prague, till I had a captain of horse from an illustrious Danish family by the scruff of the neck and had brought him out of the press to my baggage wagon. I and my horse, to be sure, received hard blows, but did not leave a single drop of blood on the battlefield but got off with nothing more than bumps and bruises. Because I then saw that all was going so well, I readied my arms once more, chased back, and fetched me a quartermaster and common trooper, who did not realize that I was a woman till I had brought them to the above-mentioned captain of horse and my own men. I searched none of them because

1. *Gleichen*] Grimmelshausen probably means the fortresses of this name located southeast of Göttingen, not the three Gleichen fortresses in Thuringia.

2. *Lutter*] Lutter am Barenberg in the Duchy of Brunswick; the battle, in which Tilly defeated Christian IV, King of Denmark, took place on August 27, 1626.

each himself gave me what money and valuables he had; I had them treat the captain of horse in particular almost politely and would not let him be touched, much less stripped; but when on purpose I rode a ways off, my servants exchanged clothes with the other two, because they were fitted out with excellent doublets. I should have risked yet a third sally and kept striking while the iron was hot and the battle was going on, but I did not wish to overtax my good horse. In the meantime my husband also got a little bit of plunder from those who had retired to Castle Lutter and had there surrendered unconditionally for the last time ever, so that both of us, during and after the battle, won from the enemy all in all about a thousand guilders' worth, which we straightway after the battle sealed and sent without further ado per bill of exchange to Prague, to add to my two thousand sovereigns there, because we had no need of it in the field and hoped daily to win even more booty.

The longer my husband and I were together, the fonder we grew of each other, and each counted himself fortunate because he had the other for a mate; and if we had not been ashamed, I believe I should not have strayed from his side, night or day, in the trenches, on watch, and in all engagements. We willed all our property to each other, so that the survivor (whether we had heirs or not) should inherit all from the deceased, but should also keep my nurse or mother as long as she lived, because she was serving us with great industry and loyalty. These testaments, because we had them executed in duplicate, we put into safekeeping, one in Prague with the Senate and the other in my husband's homeland in South Germany, which at that time was still flourishing and had not suffered the least bit from the war.

After this battle at Lutter we took Steinbruck, Verden, Langwedel, Rotenburg, Ottersberg, and Hoya,[3] at which last-mentioned castle,

---

3. *Steinbruck . . . Hoya*] Steinbruck, north of Hildesheim; Verden on the Aller; Langwedel, not far from Verden; Rotenburg on the Wümme, northeast of Verden; Ottersberg, situated between Bremen and Rotenburg; Hoya on the Weser.

Hoya, my husband was obliged to stay behind with several com-
mandeered troops and without baggage. But just as no danger could
ever keep me from my husband's side, so I did not wish to leave him
alone in this castle either, for fear that the lice might eat him alive,
because there were no women there to pick the vermin off the soldiery.
But our baggage stayed with the regiment, which went off to enjoy
winter quarters, where I myself should have been willing to stay and
enjoy myself too.

Now as soon as this had taken place, at the onset of winter, and as
soon as Tilly had divided his troops this way, look you, the King of
Denmark came with an army to win back during the winter what he
had lost during the summer; he took up a position at Verden, but
because this nut was too tough to crack he left this town unmolested
and gave his full attention to Castle Hoya, which he turned into a
sieve in less than seven days with more than a thousand cannon balls,
one of which hit my dear husband, thereby making me an unhappy
widow.

Chapter 12

Courage pays a high price for her high courage

Now when our side had surrendered the castle to the King, for fear it might collapse and bury us all, and was marching out, and I too was marching along with them, all in tears and full of sorrow, I was seen, to top my misfortune, by that major whom I had earlier taken prisoner from the Brunswick army at the river Main;[1] he inquired straightway of our troops about my person, and when he learned of my present condition, namely that I had but recently become a widow, he took advantage of the occasion and immediately snatched me away from our troops.

"You bloody witch!" he said. "Now I'll pay you back for the shame you caused me years ago at Höchst and teach you never again to bear arms or weapons or ever dare take a gentleman prisoner."

He looked so monstrous that I was stunned by his very appearance; but if I had been astride my black charger and had had him alone in front of me in the field, I should have ventured to teach him to whistle a different tune. In the meantime he led me among a troop of horse and placed me in the custody of the cornet, who got me to tell him everything that had happened between me and the lieutenant colonel (for this is the rank which he had since attained); he, for his part, told me that when I had taken him prisoner he had almost lost his head, or at least his majority, because he allowed a woman to take him away from the brigade, thereby causing the troops to fall into disorder and complete disarray, if he had not talked his way out of it by claiming that the woman who had captured him had cast a spell over him; finally he had resigned his commission anyway out of shame and had taken Danish service.

1. *at the river Main*] cf. Chapter 8.

The following night we lodged in quarters which had little to recommend them, at which place the lieutenant colonel, to avenge the insult to his person, as he called it, forced me to gratify his bestial lusts, for which occasion (O fie! what shameful folly) there could really be neither pleasure nor joy, since, though I did not resist too earnestly, instead of kisses he served me nothing but cuffs on the face.

The next day they suddenly fled, running like started hares with hounds in pursuit, so that I could not but imagine that Tilly was chasing them, though actually they were only fleeing for fear they might be chased. The second night they found quarters where the peasant was obliged to set the table; then my brave hero invited in some officers of his stripe, who were obliged to become his kinsmen through me, so that on this occasion my otherwise insatiable carnal lusts were sufficiently satisfied. The third night, after they had again run all day as if the devil himself were at their heels, I fared not a whit better, but much worse; for after I had survived this night and after all these stallions had rammed me till they were tired out (fie! I should be almost ashamed to tell it, if I were not doing so to honor and please you, Simplicissime!), then I was forced to engage the servants while their masters watched. Up till then I had suffered everything with patience and thought that I had deserved such because of my earlier misdeeds; but when it came to this, it was such a horrible abomination to me that I began to lament and bawl and appeal to God for help and revenge; but I found no mercy in these inhuman beasts, who, forgetful of all modesty and Christian propriety, first stripped me as naked as the day I was born and forced me to pick up a few handfuls of peas which they had strewn on the ground, which work they forced me to do by beating me with switches; indeed, they seasoned me with salt and pepper so that I was obliged to jump and flash like a donkey with a handful of thorns or nettles tied under his tail; and I truly believe that if it had not been wintertime they would have also switched me with nettles.

Hereupon they held council to decide whether they should turn me over to the rabble or have me executed as a sorceress. The latter, they thought, would do them all little honor, because they had enjoyed my body; in addition, the most reasonable ones argued (if actually in these beasts there was so much as a spark of human reason) that if the plan was to proceed with me in this manner, then the lieutenant colonel should have left me unmolested from the beginning and should have straightway delivered me into the hands of the court. Thus the judgment was that they should turn me over to the rabble of the baggage train that afternoon (for that same day they were staying camped in safety). Now when they had seen their fill of the miserable pea-gathering spectacle, I was allowed to put on my clothes again; and when I had completely finished doing so, a gentleman demanded to speak with the lieutenant colonel, and this was none other than that captain of horse whom I had taken prisoner before Lutter [2] and who had heard about my imprisonment. When he asked the lieutenant colonel about me and at the same time said that he wished to see me because I had taken him prisoner before Lutter, the lieutenant colonel straightway led him by the hand into the room and said: "There she sits, the *carogna*! [3] I am going to turn her over to the rabble shortly"; for he could not but think that the captain of horse would wish to avenge himself as cruelly on me as he himself had done. But the honorable gentleman was of a very different mind; hardly did he see me sitting there so wretchedly but he began to shake his head with a sigh.

I straightway remarked his compassion, therefore fell to my knees and begged him, for the sake of all his noble virtues, to take pity on a lady in distress and protect me from further shame. He lifted me up by the hand and said to the lieutenant colonel and his companions: "Oh, gentle friends! What have you done to this lady?"

The lieutenant colonel, who was already half besotted with beer, interrupted him and said: "What! She is a sorceress."

"Oh, sir, excuse me," answered the captain of horse, "as far as I know, she is, I believe, the legitimate daughter of brave old Count

2. *before Lutter*] cf. Chapter 11.
3. *carogna*] slut (Italian).

von T——, which same upright hero has staked body and soul, even house and hearth, on the commonweal, so that my most gracious King will not sanction having his children treated thus, whether they capture a few of our officers for the Imperial side or not. Indeed, I venture to say that her father at this moment is accomplishing more against the Emperor in Hungary than many a one who is leading a flying armada against him in the field."

"Ha!" answered the churlish lieutenant colonel, "How was I to know that? Why didn't she open her mouth?"

The other officers, who knew the captain of horse well and knew that he was not only of an illustrious Danish family but also enjoyed the highest favor with the King, begged most humbly that the captain of horse might overlook what had happened, set it aright as best as possible, and intervene so that they might not suffer any consequences from it; in return they promised to serve him whenever the occasion arose, at the risk of life and limb. All of them begged my pardon on bended knee too, but I could only forgive them with bitter tears; and so I came out of the hands of these brutes, harshly abused, to be sure, and into the hands of the captain of horse, who contrived to treat me far more politely; for without even once laying a finger on me, he presently sent me, with a servant and a trooper from his company, to a manor in Denmark which he had shortly before inherited from the sister of his mother, where I was maintained like a princess, which unexpected deliverance I owed both to my beauty and to my nurse, who without my knowledge and consent had in confidence told the captain of horse of my origin.

Chapter 13

What good days and nights the young countess enjoyed at the manor, and how she had to forgo same

I pampered my health and thawed out like one who crawls half-frozen out of the cold water and goes behind the stove or in front of the open hearth; for at that time I had nothing else in the world to do but loll about in the straw and fatten myself up like a war horse in winter quarters, so as to take the field that much more rested the following summer and to serve that much more boldly in future engagements. Through this I soon grew completely sound once more, sleek of skin, and yearning for my knight. And indeed, he arrived soon enough, before the long nights had altogether passed, because he could await sweet spring with no more patience than I.

When he visited me he came with four servants, of whom, however, only one was allowed to see me, namely the one who had first brought me there. No one will believe with what heart-rending words he swore to the compassion he felt for me because I had been placed into the troublesome state of widowhood, with what great promises he assured me of his faithful service, and with what politeness he lamented that before Lutter he had become my prisoner body and soul.

"Most beautiful, most noble lady," he said, "as for my body, fate freed me again, to be sure, almost immediately but left me nevertheless in other respects completely your slave, who now has come here and desires nothing but to hear from your lips the sentence to life or death: Life, that is, if you take pity on your wretched prisoner, comfort him in his hard prison of love with your comforting compassion, and save him from death; or death, if I should not gain your mercy and live, or should perhaps be adjudged unworthy of this, your love. I counted myself blessed when you, like a second knightly Penthesilea,[1] led me out of the battle your prisoner; and only when, by the outward liberation of my person, I supposedly regained my freedom did my misery actually begin, because I could no longer look upon her who still kept my heart prisoner, particularly since I also could harbor no hope of ever seeing her again, because we were on opposite sides in the war. To this misery which I have till now suffered my witnesses are many thousands of sighs which I have since sent to my lovely enemy; and because they all expired vainly into thin air, I fell into despair by and by and would have &c."

Such and similar things my castellan uttered to persuade me to do what I desired as much as he did anyway. But because I had studied more in this kind of school and well knew that what is easily obtained is held in slight regard, I pretended to be of a very different mind than he and complained instead that as I understood the matter I was in reality his prisoner, particularly since I had no control over my own person, but was in his power. Of course, I was obliged to admit that of all the gentlemen in the world I was most indebted to him, because he had saved me from the ravishers of my honor, and I recognized too that it was my duty to repay him for his honorable and praiseworthy deed with the greatest gratitude, but if this debt must be paid under the cloak of love, with the loss of my honor, then I could not see what honor he could expect in the honorable world for said laudable deliverance of my person, or what thanks from me, adding my humble plea that he not besmirch his honor through a deed which he would perhaps soon repent, nor burden the great fame of an honorable gentleman with the memory of having forced a poor deserted woman, in his house, against her will, to &c. And with that I commenced to weep as if I were most surely in dead earnest, according to the old rhyme:

1. *Penthesilea*] Queen of the Amazons, slain by Achilles.

> Women weep with moans and sighs,
> But see! Their tears are only lies,
> For they but feign that they fare ill:
> Women can weep when e'er they will.

Indeed, that he might esteem me even higher, I offered him a thousand sovereigns for my ransom if he would leave me unmolested and grant me safe passage back to my side. But he answered that his love for me was such that he would not take the whole kingdom of Bohemia in exchange for my person; in addition, he was really not in any way inferior to me in regard to family and descent, so that there really need be no great difficulty concerning a marriage between us.

Naturally, we two gave every appearance of being two doves which have been locked in a dovecote so that they may mate and which at first tire themselves out, till they finally come to an agreement, and that is just the way we acted too; for after I decided that I had resisted long enough, I became so tame and tractable towards this young paramour, who could not have been more than twenty-two years old, that in return for his golden promises I agreed to everything he desired. Indeed, I pleased him so well that he remained with me an entire month; but no one knew why, except the one above-mentioned servant and an old stewardess, who took care of me and was obliged to address me as "Her Grace, the Countess". There I conducted myself like the old proverb says:

> A tailor on a roan,
> A whore on a throne,
> A louse on a high coiffure,
> Think they do not have their peer.

My lover visited me that winter often enough, and if he had not been ashamed to do so, I believe he would even have hung up his sword for good, but he feared both his father and the King himself, since the latter was taking the war most seriously, though with slight success. But he was so indiscreet with his visits and came so often that his venerable father and mother finally noticed it and after diligent inquiry found out what kind of magnet, kept secretly by him in his manor, was

4. Duel with Swords and Poignards. From *Capricci.* 1618

drawing his weapons away from the war so frequently. Therefore they inquired most thoroughly about the character of my person and felt great anxiety for their son, for fear that he might throw himself away on me and be trapped by one who would bring little honor to their illustrious house; therefore they desired to put a stop quickly to such a marriage and yet to act so prudently that they would neither do me harm nor offend my relatives, in case perhaps, as the stewardess had told them, I really did derive from the family of a count and in case their son had already promised me marriage.

The first attack in this campaign was this: The old stewardess very confidentially warned me that my beloved's parents had found out that their son was secretly keeping a sweetheart whom he planned to wed, against their (his parents') wishes, which they could not countenance at all, since they had already promised to marry him into a very illustrious family, and therefore they were of a mind to have me abducted, but what further plans they had for me were not yet known to her. With this, I admit, the old crone quite frightened me, but not only did I not show my fear, I even pretended to be in such good spirits as if the Grand Mogul of India were prepared, if not to protect me, then at least to avenge me, particularly since I was depending on the great love and grand promises of my lover, from whom I received every week not only ardent love letters but also each time very considerable presents. I, for my part, complained to him in my reply about what I had learned from the stewardess, with the plea that he should deliver me from this danger and prevent an affront to me or my family.

The result of this correspondence was that finally two menservants dressed in my paramour's livery hurriedly arrived, bringing me a letter which said that I should immediately accompany them to Hamburg, where he would lead me publicly to the altar, whether his parents liked it or not; once this had been done, both father and mother would likely be obliged to give their consent and come to terms with matters as best they could. Straightway I was as ready to go off like a loaded cannon and let them carry me, traveling day and night, first to Wismar[2] and from there to Hamburg, where my two servants stole away, leaving me to look about as long as I wished for a gentleman from Denmark who would marry me. Only then did I realize that lightning had struck and that the fraud herself had been defrauded. Indeed, I was told that I should bear it in silence and with all patience and thank God that the worthy bride had not been drowned in the sea on the way, otherwise the bridegroom's family was still powerful enough to teach me a trick fit for such a woman as they knew I must be held to be, even in the city in which I perhaps vainly imagined that I was safe.

What could I do? My wedding, my hopes, my dreams, and everything at which I had aimed were gone and altogether ruined. The letters full of intimacies and love which I had sent to my sweetheart from time to time had been intercepted by his parents, and the answers, in turn, which I had received had been sent by them, to get me to the place where I was now sitting, gradually beginning to keep company with starvation, which easily persuaded me that even to live from hand to mouth I must find a night's wages to pay for my daily bread.

2. *Wismar*] city on the Baltic, in Mecklenburg-Schwerin.

Chapter 14

What else Courage did and how she comes into the company of a musketeer after the death of two troopers

I know not how my lover liked it when he did not find me at his manor, whether he laughed or cried. I was sorry that I could no longer enjoy his company, and I believe that he too would have been satisfied to make do with me a while longer, if only his parents had not so quickly snatched the meat from his jaws.

At this time Wallenstein, Tilly, and Count Schlick[1] overflowed all of Holstein and other Danish lands with a deluge of Imperial troops, whom the citizens of Hamburg, as well as those of other towns, were obliged to assist with provisions and ammunition, for which reason there was a great deal of riding in and out of town and for me a considerable number of customers. Finally I found out that my adopted mother was still with the army, but that all my baggage was lost except a few horses, which threw my compass off considerably. To be sure, I was faring well in Hamburg, and never in my life could I have wished for better business, but because such good *Fortuna* could last only as long as the armed forces remained in the land I was obliged to try to arrange my affairs differently too. A young trooper was then visiting me who seemed to me very amiable, resolute, and with well-lined pockets. For him I set all my snares and used every hunter's trick, till I had him in the toils and so enamored that he would have gladly eaten lettuce out of the palm of my hand without any qualms. He promised me marriage, or might the devil fetch him, and would indeed have led

1. *Schlick*] Heinrich Schlick, Count of Passau (zu Passau) and Weiszkirchen (d. 1653); a field marshal–general who participated in Wallenstein's campaign in Jutland, Schleswig, and Holstein.

me straightway to the altar in Hamburg if he had not been obliged to first ask the consent of his captain of horse, which he obtained without difficulty when he brought me to the regiment, so that he was but waiting the time and opportunity to have the ceremony performed.

In the meantime, all his companions wondered whence fortune had sent him such a beautiful young mistress, and most of them would have liked very much to become his kinsmen through me, for at that time the troops of this victorious army had grown so fat and full with plenty, because of the continuing fortunate state of affairs and abundant booty, that the greatest part, driven by prickings of the flesh, were wont to indulge themselves more in carnal pleasures and in planning for them than in looking for booty or trying to get bread and forage; and one who was particularly of this state of mind was my bridegroom's corporal, a regular brigand, and because he was particularly keen on that kind of dainty and almost made a profession of cuckolding others, he would have counted it a great disgrace to himself if he ever had attempted to do this and not succeeded at it.

At that time we were camped in Stormarn,[2] which had never yet known what war was, and it was therefore still living in abundance and was rich in food, over which we made ourselves masters, regarding the countryfolk as our thralls, cooks, and scullions. Every day and every night was a feast, and every trooper invited his friends to enjoy the food and drink which his landlord must needs serve. This was also the *modum* of my bridegroom, whereupon said hot-blooded corporal plotted to get under my skin, for when my bridegroom was making merry in his quarters with two of his companions (who, however, happened to be the corporal's toadies), the corporal came and ordered him to stand watch at the colors, so that he could amuse himself with me while my bridegroom was absent. But because my bridegroom soon saw through the trick and did not intend to let another take his place, or (to speak in plain language) to let the corporal cuckold him, look you, he told him that there were several others who by rights should stand this watch before it was his turn. But the corporal, for his part, told

2. *Stormarn*] southern Holstein, north of Hamburg.

5. Officer with Sword. From *Varie Figure*. 1617–1621

him he should not waste time in argument but obey his order, or he
would make him find his legs, for he did not want to let this fine
opportunity to possess me slip through his fingers. But since my beloved
did not intend to grant him this, he resisted the corporal till he drew
his sword to force him to stand watch or, by virtue of his authority,
to make such an example of him that the next time another would
know to what extent an inferior owed obedience to his superior. But,
alas! My dear heart took this the wrong way, for he was just as quick
to draw his sword and presented the corporal with a cut on the head
which soon enough rid him of his lewd and hot blood and so drove
out the prickings of the flesh that I could well feel safe in his presence.
The two guests went at my bridegroom with their blades and to the
aid of their corporal when he cried out for help; one of them he
presently ran through, the other he chased from the house, but the
latter straightway returned, bringing along not only the leech for
the wounded but also several lads who took my beloved and me to the
provost, where he was locked hand and foot in irons and chains.
They made short shrift of him, for the next day he was court-martialed,
and though it was clear as day that the corporal had ordered him to
stand watch for the sole purpose of sleeping with me that same night,
nevertheless the judgment was that my bridegroom should be hanged,
to preserve obedience towards officers, and I should be whipped out of
camp, because I had been the cause of such a deed. However, mercy was
granted us to the extent that my bridegroom was put before a firing
squad, and I was marched from the regiment by the provost marshal,
which journey was not at all to my taste.

But as sour a taste as this journey put into my mouth, there were
nevertheless two troopers from our camp who wished to make it
sweeter for me and for themselves; for hardly had I walked an hour
when there they were, the two of them, sitting in a thicket through
which I must needs pass, waiting to welcome me. Now all my living
days—if I must tell the truth—I have never been so choosy as to deny
a good lad a ride when he felt the need, but since these two dogs

desired to obtain from me by force, in the midst of my misfortune, the very thing for which I was being banished and my chosen one shot, I resisted violently; for I could well imagine that once they had gotten and had their way they would also have robbed me, which design I could almost read in their eyes and faces, particularly since they were not ashamed to attack me like their enemy, with drawn sabres, both to frighten me and to compel me to do what they sought. But because I knew that their sharp blades could do me less harm than two switches, look you, I armed myself with my two knives, taking one in each hand, and so met them that the one had one of them sticking in his heart before he knew it. The other was stronger and more cautious than the first, wherefore I could not get any closer to him than he to me.

We raised a hue and cry during this battle, he calling me a whore, a slut, a witch, and even a devil, and I, for my part, calling him a knave, a rapist, and whatever other pretty titles came to my lips, which brawl lured cross-country through the thicket to us a musketeer, who long stood and watched the strange leaps we were making at each other, not knowing which party he should assist or give aid to; and when we caught sight of him, each of us demanded that he should save him from the other. Now anybody can well imagine that Mars much preferred to assist Venus rather than Vulcan, especially since I straightway promised him mountains of gold and blinded and conquered him with my exceeding beauty. He waited his chance, took aim at the trooper, and by this threat succeeded in forcing him not only to turn his back on me, but even to begin to run so that the soles nearly dropped off his shoes, leaving behind his lifeless companion to wallow in his blood.

Now when the trooper had gone his way and we were alone together, this young musketeer was struck dumb, as it were, by my beauty and did not have the heart to speak to me, except to ask me by what fate I had come to be so quite alone with this trooper. Thereupon I told him everything, to the smallest detail that had happened to my late bridegroom, *item* to the corporal, and then also to me, then how these troopers, namely the one now dead and the other who had fled, had intended to violate, by force, a poor deserted woman, but against whom I had defended myself gallantly till now, as he himself had indeed seen in part, adding the plea that he, my friend in need and the savior of my honor, might help protect me further, till I should come to safety again somewhere among reputable people. I also further assured him that I would not fail to reward him for his help and assistance with respectable recompense. He thereupon searched the corpse and took what valuables he had, which rewarded him pretty well for his trouble. Thereupon we two shook the dust from our heels, and by taxing our feet almost beyond endurance we came through the thicket that much sooner and that same evening reached the musketeer's regiment, which stood ready to march into Italy with Collalto, Aldringer, and Gallas.[3]

3. *Collalto . . . Gallas*] Rambold XIII, Count of Collalto (1579–1630), Generalissimo of the Imperial army sent to Italy; Johann Aldringer (d. 1634, possibly shot by his own troops), a colonel, he led the main body of the army; Matthias, Count of Gallas (1589–1647), leader of the vanguard.

Chapter 15

Under what conditions they promise each other to live unmarried in marriage

If I had had an honest bone in my body, I could have arranged my affairs differently at that time and steered a more honorable course, for my adopted mother, with two of my remaining horses and a bit of cash money, ascertained my whereabouts and advised me to get out of the war and to my money in Prague or to the estates of my husband, the late captain of infantry, to live in peace and quiet as a householder; but there was no talking either rhyme or reason to my heedless youth, but rather the stronger the brew the better I liked the beer. I and my aforementioned mother were staying with a sutler[1] of the same regiment in which my husband who had fallen at Hoya[2] had been a captain of infantry, where they paid me due respect on his account; and I believe too that I would have gotten another good officer as husband if we had stayed quiet and lain in quarters anywhere. But because our forces of twenty thousand men, consisting of three columns, were marching to Italy with all haste and were obliged to break through Graubünden,[3] which presented many obstacles, look you, few with any brains thought of marrying, and therefore I too remained a widow much longer; on top of that, some did not have the heart to speak to me of marriage, and others had other reasons to forbear to do so, and they thought me too reputable to expect anything from me out of wedlock, because I had kept faith with my former husband, so that one and all thought me more virtuous than I was.

1. *sutler*] a provisioner to the army who traveled with it.
2. *Hoya*] cf. Chapters 10 and 11.
3. *Graubünden*] Alpine region in Switzerland.

But while I was poorly served by this long fast, on the other hand that musketeer who had come to my aid during the engagement with the two above-mentioned troopers had become so smitten with me and was making such a fool of himself over me that he had no peace, neither night nor day, and undertook many a march on my account, whenever he had time or was off duty. I well saw what was going on with him and where the shoe was pinching him; but because he did not have the courage to reveal his wishes to Courage, I felt as much contempt as pity for him. But by and by I changed my proud mind, which in the beginning was set on being nothing but an officer's lady; for when I observed the sutler's trade and saw daily with my own eyes what profits always came his way, while many an honest officer was obliged to pull in his belt, I began to ponder how I might start and institute such a sutlery myself. I made an estimate of the money and property which I had with me and found them quite sufficient, because I still had a considerable number of gold coins sewn into my bodice. Only the honor, or the disgrace, namely that from the wife of a captain of infantry I should sink to the rank of a sutler woman, held me back; but when I remembered that at this time I was no longer the wife of a captain and perhaps would not attain to such a rank again either, look you, then the die was cast, and I was already seeing myself in my mind's eye serving up wine and beer at double the price and haggling worse than a fifty- or sixty-year-old Jew.[4]

Just at this time, namely when we had arrived in Italy, having traversed the *Alpes,* or high mountains, with our three-pronged Imperial army, my gallant's passion reached the highest peak, without his having yet spoken a single word to me about it. Once, under the pretext of drinking a measure of wine, he came to my sutler's tent, looking pale and disconsolate, as if he had but recently had a baby without having either father, milk, or pap for it, nor knowing where

---

4. *Jew*] Grimmelshausen shares the prejudice of his time against other nations. In the case of Jews he seems to confine his bias to the notion that they are invariably avaricious and dishonest traders.

to come by them. His sad glances and his ardent sighs were the best language he spoke to me, and when I asked him what he desired, he took heart and answered me immediately as follows: "Oh, my most beloved captain's lady (for he dared not call me Courage), if I should tell you my desire, I should either arouse your ire, so that you would straightway deprive me of your lovely presence and never again ever deign to look upon me, or you would reprove me for my transgression, either of which would most assuredly mean certain death for me." And thereupon he again became as silent as a grave.

I answered: "If either of them can mean certain death for you, then each of them can also revive you; and because I am indebted to you for having saved me from my ravishers when we lay in Vierlanden,[5] between Hamburg and Lubeck, I therefore gladly grant you the privilege of looking upon me till you are hale and hearty once more."

"Oh, most esteemed lady!" he answered, "The very opposite is true, for when I looked upon you for the first time, the sickness began which will be the death of me if I should no longer look upon you. Truly a wonderful and strange state which I have fallen into in recompense for having saved my most esteemed lady from the danger which had befallen her."

I said I should be guilty of great ingratitude if I had thus rewarded good with evil.

"That I do not say," answered my musketeer.

I replied: "What then are you complaining of?"

"Of myself, of my unhappiness," he answered, "and of my fate, or perhaps of my impertinence, or of my fancy, or of I myself know not what. I cannot say that the captain's lady is ungrateful, because for the trifling trouble I took in driving off the trooper who was yet alive and threatening her honor I was sufficiently rewarded by the legacy of the trooper whom my most esteemed lady had already so gloriously deprived of his life, so that he should not shamefully deprive her of her honor. My sovereign mistress," he said further, "I am in such a

5. *Vierlanden*] a marshy region southeast of Hamburg.

6. Two Women. From *Capricci.* 1618

perturbed state, which so perturbs me that I can neither explain my perturbation, nor my desires, nor my guilt or indebtedness or your own, much less my own guiltlessness, or anything at all which might help me. Behold, most beauteous lady, I am dying because fortune and my low estate do not grant me the joy of showing your Highness how happy I should esteem myself to be your most humble servant."

I stood there like a fool, because I had heard from a lowly and still very young musketeer such a speech, all mixed up and, as he said, proceeding from a perturbed mind; nevertheless it seemed to me to reveal a lively spirit and an ingenious mind which was worthy of my love and which seemed to me would be profitable for me to use in good faith in the sutlery with which my belly was teeming at that time. Therefore I made short shrift of the poor booby and said to him: "My friend, first you call me your sovereign mistress; secondly, you call yourself my servant, if you only could be that; thirdly, you lament that without me you must die: Now from these I recognize the great love which you perhaps bear me. Now just tell me how I may requite this love, for towards one who has saved me from my ravishers I do not wish to be found wanting in gratitude."

"With love," said my gallant, "and if I be found worthy of it I should count myself the happiest man in the whole world."

I answered: "You have yourself confessed, first of all, that to stay with me your estate is lower than you would wish it to be, and whatever else you have given me to understand in your long-winded discourse. But what is to be done to help you, to free me from any accusation of ingratitude and you from your suffering?"

He answered that for his part the decision should be mine, particularly since he held me to be not an earthly creature but a goddess from whom he was prepared to gladly accept the sentence of either life or death, *servitut* or liberty, indeed anything and everything which it pleased me to command. And this he indicated to me with such gestures that I could well perceive that I had a monkey on a chain who would rather choke to death in his willingness to serve me than live in freedom without me.

I pursued what I had begun and did not hesitate to fish in troubled waters; and why shouldn't I have, since after all the devil himself undertakes to get completely into his nets those who are in the state in which my beau found himself? I do not say this so that an honest Christian should find an example in me and copy the actions of the evil fiend just because I was imitating him at that time, but so that Simplicius, to whom alone I am dedicating this, my life history, may see what kind of lady he loved when he loved me. And listen closely, Simplex, and you will find out that I repaid you for that fine trick you played on me in Sauerbrunnen, so that for every pound you gave you got a hundredweight in return. But this gallant of mine I cajoled into agreeing to, and promising to hold to, the following points.

First of all, he was to obtain a discharge from his regiment, for otherwise he could not be my servant, since I did not wish to be the wife of a musketeer.

Then, secondly, he was to live with me and show toward me all the love and faithfulness that a husband is wont to show toward his wife, as I should toward him in return.

However, thirdly, this union was not to be confirmed in the Christian church till I first found myself with child by him.

Till then, fourthly, I was to have and hold authority in every way and form, not only over the provisions but also over my own body, indeed even over my *serviteur* himself, in just the way a husband usually has jurisdiction over his wife.

In consequence, fifthly, he was not to have the power to hinder or prevent it, much less look askance at it, if I should converse with other men or do anything of the sort that commonly causes husbands to wax wroth.

And because, sixthly, I was of a mind to play the role of a sutler woman, he was of course to be the head of this enterprise and direct it like a faithful and diligent householder, by day and by night, but let me have the last word, particularly about the money and himself, and obey patiently, and even change his ways and improve himself if I were to reprimand him for his laziness. *In summa*, he was to be considered and looked upon by one and all as the master and was to have this title and honor too, but toward me observe every one of the above-mentioned duties in every respect. And all this we both signed and sealed.

And so that he might remember his duty toward me at all times, he was to suffer, as a seventh point, that I call him by a special name, which name was to be formed from the first words of the command by which I should the first time order him to do something.

Now when he had agreed to all these points and had sworn to hold to them, I confirmed it with a kiss, but for the time being permitted him no further liberties. Soon afterwards he brought me his discharge; I, for my part, got down to work and arranged with another infantry regiment for everything which a sutler should have and began to ply the Jew's trade as if I had been at it all my life.

Chapter 16

How Hopalong and Courage kept house with each another

My young man showed excellent promise in everything for which I had taken him on and was using him; thus he also kept to the abovementioned articles so nicely and proved himself so obedient that I did not have the least cause to complain of him. Indeed, when he could divine what might be my desire he was straightway eager to fulfill it; for he was so besotted in his love for me that he neither heard with his ears wide open nor saw with his eyes wide open what he had in me and I in him; but rather he believed that he had the most gentle, most faithful, most reasonable, and most modest sweetheart on earth, in which belief my adopted mother, whom he held in high regard on my account, was able to strengthen him and help me. She was much slyer than a fox, much greedier than a wolf, and I cannot say whether she was more proficient in the art of making money or in the art of pandering. If I had a lewd plan of that sort in mind and felt a bit of apprehension (for I wished to be regarded as very gentle and modest), I had only to confide it to her and it was as good as assured that my wish would be carried out; for her conscience could encompass as much as the thighs of the Rhodesian Colossus, which were spread so far apart that the largest ship could sail in between them without striking sail.[1]

Once I had great lust to enjoy a young man of nobility who was a cornet at that time and had recently given me to understand that he loved me; at just that time when this desire arose in me, we had made camp near a village, for which reason everyone, including my rabble,

1. *Colossus . . . sail*] Courage is wrong in assuming that the legs of this huge statue straddled the entrance to the harbor; it stood at the entrance.

left the camp to fetch wood and water; but my sutler was busying himself about the wagon, having just pitched my tent and put our horses with the others in the pasture close to us. Now because I had revealed my wishes to my mother, she arranged for this same cornet to be at hand, though not at the proper time; and when he came the first thing I asked him in the presence of my husband was whether he had any money. And when he answered, "Yes," for he thought that I was already asking a *salva venia*[2] for whore's wages, I said to my sutler: "Hop along and catch our piebald! The cornet here would like to ride him and bargain for him for cash."

Now while my good sutler obediently went to carry out this first command of mine, the old crone kept watch while we made the sale with each other and paid each other off valiantly. But since it was not as easy for my sutler to catch the horse as it was for the cornet to catch the sutler's woman, he came back to the tent all tired out and as impatient as the cornet pretended to be on account of the long wait. Because of this story said cornet later composed a song called "The Piebald," beginning with the words: "Oh, what inexpressible torture ... &c," with which later on Germany was burdened for several years, because no one knew where it had originated. My sutler, however, received on the strength of our marriage contract the name "Hopalong,"[3] and this is the same Hopalong whom you, Simplicissime, repeatedly praise as a good fellow in your life history. You must know too that all those little tricks which you and he practiced, both in Westphalia[4] and at Phillipsburg, and many more besides he learned from none other than me and my old mother; for when I paired up with him he was simpler than a sheep, and when he left us he was more cunning than any lynx or archrogue can be.

But to tell the truth, he did not come by such science for nothing,

2. *salva venia*] with your indulgence.
3. *Hopalong*] the German is *Springinsfeld*, literally "jump in the field," and it is used to describe a carefree, flighty youth. The translators make no apologies for their English rendering.
4. *Westphalia*] see *Simplicissimus*, Book II, Chapter 31.

but first had to pay me a proper apprentice fee. Once, while he was still all simplicity, he and I and my mother were discoursing on the deceit and malice of women, and he was impudent enough to maintain that no woman could ever deceive him, however cunning she might be. Now though he was clearly demonstrating his simplicity sufficiently by saying this, it nevertheless appeared to me that such talk was too disparaging and insulting to the dexterity of myself and all clever women, and therefore I told him candidly that I deemed myself capable of deceiving him nine times before morning soup, if only I wished to. He, on the other hand, was audacious enough to say that if I should be able to do so he would be my slave for his whole life long, and even dared me to do it, but with the proviso that if during such a span of time I could not practice any of the nine deceptions I should then let him lead me to the altar and be wedded to him. Now after we had thus made our wager I came to him early the next morning with the soup dish, in which lay the bread, and in the other hand the knife and the whetstone, with the request that he sharpen the knife a little so that I could cut the bread for the soup. He took the knife and the stone from me, and because he had no water he licked the whetstone to moisten it. Then I said: "Well, by God, that's twice already!"

He was surprised and asked what I meant by that. I, for my part, asked him if he could no longer remember our wager of yesterday. He answered: "Yes," and asked whether and how then I had already deceived him.

I answered: "First of all, I dulled the knife so that you would be obliged to sharpen it again; secondly, I rubbed the whetstone on a place you can easily imagine and then gave it to you to slobber over with your tongue."

"Oho!" he said. "If it has gone this far already, just hush and stop; I gladly declare you the winner and do not wish to hear about the rest of the tricks."

So now I had in my Hopalong a slave; by night, when I had nothing else better, he was my mate, by day my servant, and when people

7. Cannon. From *Military Exercises*, 1632

were watching, my lord and master in every respect. He even sub-
mitted so nicely to this arrangement and to my humor that I could not
have wished for any better husband in all my life, and I should have
been more than glad to marry him too, if I had not worried that he
might thereby shake off the reins of obedience and, in asserting the
mastery over me which would then be rightfully his, pay me back a
hundredfold for whatever I had done to him while we were still unmarried and what he had doubtless been obliged to suffer at times with
much vexation. In the meantime we lived together as harmoniously,
but not as saintly, as the angels. My mother served as the sutler's
woman in my stead, I as the beautiful cook or maidservant whom
mine host keeps in the loft to attract many guests. My Hopalong, on
the other hand, was master and servant or whatever else I wished him
to be. He was obliged to pay me strict obedience and to follow the
counsel of my mother; for the rest, all my rabble, of whom I had
more than many a captain of infantry, obeyed him as their master. We
had slovenly commissary butchers with the regiment who were wont
to rather drink up their money instead of making it; therefore I
weaseled my way into their profession through bribery and kept two
butchers of my own for the price of one, so that I alone received
preference and by and by ruined the others, because I could provide
every guest, no matter where he came from, with a piece of any kind
of meat he wished, no matter whether it be raw, boiled, roasted, or live.

When it came to stealing, robbing, and plundering (and what
beautiful booty could not be found in full and rich Italy!), then not
only Hopalong together with my rabble were obliged to risk their
necks to fetch it in, but Courage herself went back to the old ways she
had practiced in Germany, and by thus fighting against the enemy
with soldier's arms and against my friends in camp with a Jew's
weapons and keeping up my guard even during the friendliest sort of
engagement, my purse grew so fat that I was obliged to send a bill of
exchange of a thousand crowns to Prague almost every month,
without myself or mine ever suffering want; for I diligently saw to it

that my mother, my Hopalong, my other rabble, and particularly my horses always had plenty of food, clothing and feed, even if I myself should have been obliged to go hungry and naked and live under the open sky, by day and by night. They, for their part, were obliged to earn me a profit and not to slack, neither day nor night, in this labor, even if they should have lost life and limb at it.

Chapter 17

What a ridiculous prank was played on Courage, and how she avenged herself

Look you, Simplice, thus I was already the concubine and teacher of your companion, Hopalong, when you were perhaps still herding your daddy's swine and before you were clever enough to be other peoples' fool, and yet you dare to imagine that you deceived me in Sauerbrunnen! After the first siege of Mantua[1] we were assigned our winter quarters in a merry little town where I began to have a pretty good number of customers. There was not a banquet or a feast at which Courage was not present, and where she appeared the Italian *puttane*[2] counted for naught; for to the Italians I was fair game and something new, with the Germans I could speak their language, and towards both nations I was far too friendly, besides still being exceeding beautiful; also I was neither so very arrogant nor expensive, and no one had to worry about trickery with me, while by contrast the Italian women were full of deceit. These qualities of mine were responsible for my unhitching many good fellows from the carts of the Italian whores, which gentlemen forsook them and visited me instead, which did not endear me to them. Once I was invited to supper by a distinguished gentleman who had formerly been attached to the most famous *puttana*, but had forsaken her for me. Of this meat she in turn thought to deprive me and to that end had a furrier's wife put something in the food I ate during said meal which made my belly swell up as if it were about to burst; indeed, the belly vapors so oppressed me that in the end they forced the gate, causing such lovely music to be heard

1. *Mantua*] besieged in the winter of 1629–1630.
2. *puttane*] prostitutes (Italian).

during the meal that I was sore ashamed; and once they had found the
gate, they passed through it one after the other with such enthusiasm
that it kept on thundering as if several regiments at once were firing
off a salvo. Now when I therefore arose from the table to run away, this
physical activity really started it in earnest: At every step at least one
escaped me, or ten, though in truth they followed upon one another
so swiftly that no one could count them, and I believe that if I had been
able to keep them in good order and properly spaced I could have
beaten for two whole hours by the clock a better tattoo than the best
drummer. But this way it only lasted for about a half an hour, during
which time both guests and stewards suffered more torment from
laughing than I did from my continued trumpeting.

This prank I reckoned a great affront to myself and was about to
bolt for shame and ill humor; my host felt the same way, since he had
invited me for a different purpose than to hear this beautiful music,
swearing by all that is holy that he would avenge this affront, if only he
could find out what peppercorn-ant-eggs cook had struck up this
harmonia inside me. But because I was in doubt as to whether he himself might not have contrived the whole sorry business, look you, I sat
in such a sulk as if I intended to kill everyone with the lightning flashes
of my angry eyes, till I finally learned from a guest sitting next to me
that the above-mentioned furrier's wife knew how to practice such
medicine; and because he had seen her below stairs, he reasoned that
she had somehow been engaged by some jealous lady to make me
repugnant to this or that gentleman by means of this prank, particularly
since she was known to have done the very same thing to a rich
merchant, who had lost favor with his ladylove because of such music,
because he had played it in her presence and in the presence of other
respectable people. Thereupon I was satisfied and deliberated on swift
revenge, which, however, must not be public or inhuman, because we
were obliged (despite the fact that we were occupying enemy territory)
to keep good order in our quarters.

Now after I had ascertained the truth, namely that it had happened

8. Lady and Cavaliers from the Court of France. From *Fantasies*. 1633

just as the above-mentioned table companion had suspected, I inquired as exactly as I could about the comings and goings, the ways and habits of that lady who had played this prank on me, and when I was shown the window from which she was wont to give nightly audience to those who wished to visit her, I revealed the grievance I nursed her to two officers; they, if they wished to further enjoy my favors at all, were obliged to promise me to execute my revenge, and as a matter of fact, in such and no other wise as I prescribed to them; for it seemed to me that it would be just, since she had vexed me only with the vapors, that I should pay her back with nothing less than the muck itself. And this happened in the following way: I had a bull's bladder filled with the worst kind of ordure which can be found in the upside-down chimneys by Master Arsehole's sweeps. This was tied to a stick or sort of flexible pole which is commonly used to knock nuts off trees or to clean the soot out of chimneys, and in the dark of night, while one of my cohorts was paying court to the *puttana*, who was as usual at her audience window up above, the other smashed her in the face with it with such force that the bladder burst, and the muck bespattered her nose, eyes, mouth, and bosom, together with all her ornaments and jewelry, after which prank both the suitor as well as the *executor* ran off, leaving the whore at the window to wail as long as she wished.

The wife of the furrier I paid back this way: Her husband was wont to collect and save every hair, even if it came from a cat, as carefully as if he had shorn it off the golden ram fleece of the Island of Colchis, so much so that he did not throw away a shred of skin, whether it be beaver, hare, or lamb, till he had first plucked it clean of all hair or wool. And then when he had a few pounds together the hatter gave him money for it, which indeed supplied his house with a few crumbs, and even though it was a trifling sum and went slowly, it still amounted to a bit in time. This I learned from another furrier who was lining a fur coat for me that same winter; therefore I got as much of such wool and hair as I needed and used it in the privy for a certain purpose. When it was ready, or to explain more closely, when these bits and pieces had been well salved and were as full of a certain material as the bottles and tins of a quacksalver are,[3] I had one of my boys scatter them around the furrier's privy, or *secret* as it is called, which was open a good ways above the ground. Now when this penny-pinching householder saw the clumps of hair and wool lying below, inside and out, and took them to be his own, he could not but imagine that his wife had spoiled and dishonored them thus. He therefore began to rage at her as if she had already destroyed and lost Mantua and Casale[4] to the enemy, and because she denied everything as stubbornly as a witch and even answered spitefully, he beat her till she was as soft as leather, even though he was gentle in preparing the skins of other wild and ravenous beasts, not to mention the native cat skins, all of which pleased me so well that I should not have taken a dozen crowns instead.

Now the only one left was the apothecary whom I suspected of having prepared the recipe through which I had been obliged to raise on high such a variable voice from the nether regions; for he kept songbirds which ate feed that is supposed to have the effect of causing such a clamor as I have described. But because he was well liked both by officers and noncommissioned officers, particularly since we must needs use his services every day for our sick, who could not stand the Italian air, and also because I myself must worry that I might have to take his cure any day, I dared not rub him the wrong way too openly; nevertheless, I could not and would not stomach so many airy sprites, who, to be sure, had long since scattered into thin air, but cast about for a revenge to wreak, even though others had been obliged to put up with the reek of the airy sprites once I had stomached them. He had a small vaulted cellar under his house in which he kept all kinds of wares which because of their nature must be kept in such a place. Into this cellar I directed water from a fountain in a nearby square by tying one

3. *bottles . . . quacksalver*] it was then believed that the patient's excrement was a potent antidote.

4. *Casale*] on the Po River; at that time an important fortress.

end of a long ox gut to the fountain and hanging the other end down inside the cellar window and letting the water run through it the whole long winter night, so that the next morning the cellar was full to overflowing. There one saw several casks of Malvoisier and Spanish wine and anything which was light swimming about; but everything which could not float lay ruined under six feet of water; and because I had the gut removed before break of day, everyone thought the next morning either that a spring had welled up in the cellar or that this trick had been played on the apothecary through sorcery. But I knew better, and because I had planned and executed everything so well I laughed up my sleeve while the apothecary lamented his spoiled *materialia.* And at that time I was glad that the name "Courage" had taken such deep root, otherwise the scallawags would no doubt have called me the General Fartress, because I do it better than anyone else.

Chapter 18

About the quite too overweening godlessness of unscrupulous Courage

The profits which came my way through such varied trades were so to my liking that the longer I plied these trades the more profit I desired; and since it was already all the same to me whether I made my profit by honest or dishonest means, I began not to care either whether the business might better be pursued with God's help or Mammon's. Finally I cared little through what kind of advantage, what kind of holds, with what kind of conscience, and by what kind of manipulations I prospered, just as long as I became rich. My Hopalong was obliged to play the horse trader, and what he did not know he was obliged to learn from me, since in this profession I practiced a thousand different roguish, thieving, and fraudulent tricks. No ware, neither of gold, silver, jewelry, much less of tin, copper, cloth, clothing or whatever else it might be, no matter whether it be legitimate booty, robbed or even stolen, was too dear or too cheap for me to trade for; and whenever someone did not know where to go to turn what he had into silver, no matter whether he had come by it by fair means or foul, he was sure to find an outlet with me as easily as with any Jew, and Jews are more loyal to thieves to safeguard them than they are to the magistrate in helping to punish them. Therefore my two wagons resembled too much a general market not to contain much more than mere expensive *victualia*, and for just that reason I, for my part, was also able to supply any soldier, no matter whether he be high or low in rank, with anything he needed for cash in hand. On the other hand, I was obliged to make gifts and to grease many a palm to protect myself and my affairs: The provost was "my dear father," his old *mère*[1] (his old woman, I meant to say) was "my dear mother," the colonel's lady "milady," and the colonel himself "milord," and all of them protected me from anything which might have endangered me or my band or my business.

Once an old chicken thief, I meant to say "an old soldier," who had been carrying a musket long before the Bohemian fracas brought me some sort of something in a little sealed glass flask that did not rightly look like a spider or like a scorpion either; I took it to be no insect or living thing, because the flask had no air in it by which the imprisoned thing could have maintained its life, and I thought rather that it must be some sort of artful device made by an excellent master craftsman who had fashioned it to present the likeness of I know not what kind of perpetual motion, because it stirred and crawled about in the flask without rest. I prized it highly, and because the old man offered to sell it to me I asked "How much?" He offered me the piece of trash for two crowns, which I forthwith paid him too, and then offered him a measure of wine in the bargain; but he said that full payment had been made, which surprised me in such an old tippler and caused me to ask him why he was refusing the drink which, after all, I gave to anyone with whom I made a sale, however small.

"Oh, Madam Courage," he answered, "It is different with this than with other wares; it has a certain price at which it must be bought and sold, for which reason Madam must be careful when she in turn sells it, for she must needs sell it for less than she paid for it."

I said: "That way I should have little profit from it."

He answered: "Let that be your worry. As far as I am concerned, I have already owned it for thirty years or more and have never suffered any loss by it, though I bought it for three crowns and sold it again for two."

This was so much nonsense to me, and I could make neither head nor tail of it and perhaps did not wish to either; for I was fair drunk and

1. *mère*] the German is *Merr*; also a play on the French *mère* (mother) and the German *Mähre* (mare).

was expecting to entertain several emissaries of Venus; therefore it worried me but little; or (dear Reader, you tell me how I should put it) I knew not what to make of the old creak. He did not seem to me man enough to deceive Courage, and being accustomed to the fact that others who looked smarter than this old man often sold me something for one ducat that was worth a hundred made me so sure of myself that I pocketed the treasure I had bought.

Next morning, when I had slept off my drunk, I found my purchase in the pocket of my breeches (for you must know that I always wore breeches under my skirt); I remembered straightway in what manner I had bought the thing and put it therefore with the rest of my rare and lovely possessions, such as rings, jewels, and the like, to save it for the day when I should perhaps come upon a connoisseur who could inform me of its nature. But when I happened to put my hand in my pocket sometime during the day, I found it not where I had put it for safekeeping but instead in my pocket again, which astounded me more than it frightened me; and my curiosity to know what it actually was caused me to look about diligently for the old man who had sold it to me; and when I found him I asked him what he had sold me, told him besides what wondrous thing had happened with it, and begged him not to keep from me any information concerning its nature, power, effect, talents, and all the details about its properties.

He answered: "Madam Courage, it is a servant-spirit which brings great good fortune to that person who buys it and keeps it with him. It shows where hidden things are located, it procures sufficient partners for any kind of business transaction and increases prosperity, it makes its owner loved by his friends and feared by his foes. Anyone who has it and relies on it, it makes as shotfree as steel armor, and it protects from imprisonment; it brings good fortune, victory, and conquest over the enemy and makes it necessary that almost everyone love its owner."

In summa, the old lynx told me such a pack of tall tales that I thought

I was more fortunate than Fortunatus[2] with his little sack and his wishing cap. But because I could well imagine that the so-called servant-spirit would not give such gifts for nothing, I asked the old man what I must do in return to please the thing, for I had heard that those sorcerers who rob other people with the aid of a mandrake are obliged to give the so-called mandrake weekly baths and other care. The old man answered that this was not at all necessary here; there was a very great difference between a mandrake and such a thing as I had bought from him. I said that no doubt it would not be willing to be my servant and fool for nothing; he should simply reveal to me boldly and in confidence whether I might own it without any danger at all and also without rewarding it at all while I enjoyed its considerable services without making any pact with it and serving it in return.

"Madam Courage," answered the old man, "you know enough already, namely that you must sell it for less (when you have tired of its services) than you paid for it, which I did not hide from you at the time you bought it from me." And with that the old man went his way.

My Bohemian mother was at that time my most intimate counselor, my father confessor, my favorite, my best friend and my *Zabud Salomonis*:[3] I confided everything to her and therefore also what had happened to me with the treasure I had bought.

"Hah!" she answered, "It is a *stirpitus flammiarum*[4] which can

---

2. *Fortunatus*] hero of one of the best-loved German chapbooks of the sixteenth century; his good fortune was the result of his acquisition of a *Säckel* which was never empty of gold pieces and a wishing hat which could transport him in an instant to any place he wished to go.

3. *Zabud Salomonis*] ". . . and Zabud, the son of Nathan was principal officer, and the king's [Solomon's] friend" (I Kings 4:5).

4. *stirpitus flammiarum*] the Latin *spiritus familaris* is so altered by this mala-propism of Courage's Bohemian mother that it resembles the German *stirb* (die) and *Flamme* (flame, fire); she bases her interpretation of the "thing" on this similarity—whoever dies in possession of it will be condemned to the flames. Robert Louis Stevenson uses the same figure in his short story "The Bottle Imp" in the *Island Nights Entertainments* (1893).

perform everything that the man who sold it to you told you; but whosoever has it when he dies must, as I have been told, travel with it to that other world, which, to judge by its name, must without doubt be hell, where there is said to be fire and flame everywhere; and just for this reason it will let the owner sell it only for less than he paid for it, so that the last one who buys it must fall prey to it. And you, dear daughter, are in great danger, because you are the last one who can sell it; for what fool will buy it from you if he cannot sell it himself, but knows for sure that he is buying his eternal damnation from you?"

I could well appreciate that my trade had been a bad one, but my frivolity, my blooming youth, hope for a long life, and the universal godlessness of the world caused me to regard it lightly. I thought: "You will enjoy this help, this assistance, and this fortunate advantage as long as you can. In the meantime you will surely find a thoughtless fellow somewhere in this world who, either when he is drunk or because of poverty, desperation, blind hope for great good fortune, or because of avarice, lewdness, anger, envy, lust for revenge, or something like that, will take this guest off your hands for the price asked."

Accordingly, I availed myself of its help in every way and form, as had been described to me by the old man and also by my nurse, or adopted Bohemian mother. I remarked its effect daily too; for where another sutler was dispensing one barrel of wine I was selling three or four; once a customer tasted my food and drink he did not forbear to come back a second time. Whatever man I looked at and wished to enjoy was straightway ready and willing to serve me with most submissive devotion, indeed to revere me just like a goddess; when I came to a billet where the householder had fled or to some inn or deserted dwelling or other where no one else could live (particularly since the sutlers and commissary butchers were not generally lodged in palaces), then I straightway found where the loot was hidden and was able, I know not by what inner voice, to find such treasures as had not seen the light of day for many, perhaps a hundred, years. On the other hand, I cannot deny that there were some who cared nothing for

9. Pride. From *The Seven Deadly Sins*. 1619

Courage, but rather despised, in fact persecuted, rather than honored her, without a doubt because they were illuminated by a greater *lumen* than the *flamine* with which I was possessed. This did put me on my guard and taught me to philosophize and ponder, after considerable thought, how come? what for? and so on. But I was already so drowned in rapaciousness and all the vices which attend it that I left everything as it was, rather than prepare the foundation on which my eternal salvation rested, as it indeed still does today. All this, Simplice, I am telling you in excessive detail to crown your glory, because you have bragged in your biography that you enjoyed a lady in Sauerbrunnen whom you really did not even know yet.

In the meantime, as time went by, my pile of money grew larger, indeed so large that even with all my means I was afraid.

Listen, Simplice, I must remind you of something else. If you had been worth anything when we played at dalliance with one another in Sauerbrunnen, you would have been even more impervious to my wiles than those who stood under God's protection when I still owned the *Spirit. famil.*

Chapter 19

What kind of teacher Hopalong had till he attained perfection himself

And something else you must know, Simplice. Not only did I tread the above-described path, but also my Hopalong (whom you, to be sure, in your biography boasted to be your best companion and a fine fellow) was forced to follow me down it. And what should have prevented it, or why should that be a great miracle? Particularly since shiftless husbands (if I may even say "husbands"—I almost said "tame husbands") are induced (I do not wished to say "forced") by other loose womenfolk like me to perform the same kind of loose capers, even though they have not agreed to the kind of marriage contract that Hopalong agreed to. Listen to this story:

While we were lying before the famous city of Casale, Hopalong and I drove to a neighboring border town, which was neutral, to buy victuals and take them back to our camp. Now since in such cases I did not venture forth only to haggle like a true descendant of the *Hierosolymitanites*[1] but also to seek my profit like a Cyprian virgin,[2] I had therefore bedizened myself like a Jezebel too and did not care whether I might seduce an Ahab or a Jehu. To this end I entered a church, because I had been told that in Italy most affairs of the heart were instituted and nurtured in these holy places, for the reason that the beautiful women there, who seem to be worthy of love, are not allowed to go anywhere else. I came to stand beside a young lady whose beauty and jewelry I commenced to envy, because the man

1. *Hierosolymitanites*] citizens of Jerusalem.
2. *Cyprian virgin*] Cyprian girls were said to earn their dowries by soliciting sailors along the beaches.

who was casting so many a loving glance upon her did not even look at me. I confess that it cut me to the quick that he preferred her to me and that, as I imagined, I should be despised in comparison to her by a man caught in her trap. This vexation and my immediate thoughts of revenge were the greatest devotion I brought to this church service. Now before it had ended my Hopalong also arrived. But I know not why and can hardly believe either that piety drove him there, for I had not taught him that, nor was it in his nature either, nor had it been nurtured in him through the study of holy scriptures or through listening to sermons. Nevertheless, he took his place beside me and received from me the whispered command to mark where said lady had her dwelling, so that I might get possession of the surpassingly beautiful emerald which she wore around her neck.

He obeyed dutifully like a faithful servant and reported to me that she was the highborn lady of a rich gentleman who had his *palatium* by the market place. I, for my part, told him expressly that he should neither further enjoy my favor nor touch my body again a single time till he had first handed her emerald over to me, to which end, however, I was going to give him foolproof plans, means, and opportunity. Of course, he scratched his head and was frightened at my presumption, as if it were an impossible thing; but after much talking back and forth, he declared he was willing to face death for my sake.

This is how, Simplice, I trained your Hopalong like a young spaniel, as it were. He had a talent for it too, perhaps more than you, but on his own he would never have become such a paragon, if he had not gone through my school.

At that very time I was obliged to have a new handle made for my martel,[3] which I used both as a weapon and as a key to open any peasants' coffers and chests I could get at; this handle I had had hollowed out inside wide enough to fill it with either ducats or groats of the same size; and because I generally always had this martel with me

3. *martel*] a weapon with a pick at one end of the headpiece and a hammer at the other; from the French *martel de fer* (iron hammer).

(since I was no longer allowed to carry a sword and did not wish to carry a pair of pistols), I thought to stuff it inside with ducats, which I should then have on hand for all kinds of emergencies (of which there are various kinds during wartime). When it was finished I tried it out for size with a few lucernes[4] which I had taken to exchange for other money; the hollow inside of the handle had just about the circumference of these coins, but was so narrow and tight that I was obliged to force them, the lucernes, somewhat to get them into it, but with far less force than one uses to load a demicannon. But I could not fill the whole handle with them, because there were too few of them, wherefore it quite fitly happened that when the lucernes were resting against the hammer head and I held it in my hand, using the handle like a cane and leaning on it, some of the lucernes clanked down against the grip and made a dull ringing noise, which sounded strange and wondrous enough, since no one knew where the sound was coming from. Enough of long explanations. I gave my Hopalong the martel with exact instructions as to how he was to acquire the emerald for me with it.

Thereupon my Hopalong disguised himself, putting a wig on his head and wrapping himself in a borrowed black cloak, and for two whole days he did nothing but stand opposite the lady's *palatio*, looking it over from top to bottom, almost as if he had wished to buy it. Now I had also hired a drummer, who was such a sly fox that he could have outfoxed the devil himself, and he too was instructed to do nothing whatsoever but loll about the market place, keeping close watch on Hopalong all the while, in case he needed his assistance; for this gallow's bird spoke Italian just as well as he did German, which the other could not. I myself, however, had an alchemist prepare a liquid (no need to give its name here) which eats through any metal in a few hours and makes it soft or even dissolves it into water; with this I painted the thick grating over one of the cellar windows. Now when Hopalong, on the third day, still persisted in gaping at the house like a cat at a new

4. *lucernes*] Luter, a small Swiss coin.

10. Envy. From *The Seven Deadly Sins*. 1619

barn door, look you, the lady, growing curious, sent out and inquired why he kept standing there and what there was for him to see in her house. Hopalong, for his part, had the above-mentioned drummer come and interpret for him, and say that hidden in the house was a treasure which, he was confident, not only could he raise but which would also make a whole city rich. Hereupon the lady had both Hopalong and the drummer come into the house, and after she had once more listened to Hopalong's lies about hidden treasure and had conceived a great desire to have it, she asked the drummer what kind of man Hopalong was, whether he were a soldier, and so on.

"No," answered this archrogue, "he is a sort of necromancer, as they are called, and stays with the army for the sole purpose of finding hidden things, and as I have heard tell, he has also found and raised whole coffers and chests full of gold in Germany in old castles." Otherwise this man, Hopalong, was not known to him, the drummer, at all.

In summa, after a long discourse, the pig was in the poke, and it was decided that Hopalong should search for the treasure. He asked for two consecrated wax tapers, but he himself lit a third one which he had with him and which he could snuff whenever he wished by means of a brass wire that ran through it. With these three lights the lady, two of her servants, Hopalong, and the drummer lit their way around the house, for just then the master of the house was not at home; for Hopalong had persuaded her that whenever they came near the treasure his taper would go out by itself. Now when they had wandered through the whole house this way in solemn procession, Hopalong mumbling strange words at all the places they lit up with their lights, they finally came to the cellar, where I had moistened the iron grating with my A.R.;[5] there Hopalong stood facing one of the walls, and while he was going through his usual ceremonies, out went his light. "There!" he had the drummer interpret, "There the treasure is,

5. *A.R.*] *aqua regia*, a mixture of nitric and hydrochloric acids; it got its name—royal water—because it can dissolve the so-called "noble" metals such as gold.

bricked up in the wall!" Thereupon he mumbled a few more non-sensical words, striking the wall a few times with my martel, so that the lucernes rolled down inside the handle at every stroke and made their usual sound. "Listen!" he then said, "The treasure has ripened again, which happens once every seven years. It's ripe and must be raised while the sun is still in the sign of the Hedgehog,[6] otherwise it will be no use to try for another seven years."

Now because the lady and her two servants would have sworn a thousand oaths that the ringing noise had been in the wall, they placed implicit faith in my Hopalong, and the lady asked him, for a fee, to raise the treasure and was also straightway ready to make a pact with him for a certain amount. But when he allowed that in such cases he neither asked nor took anything except whatever one gave him voluntarily, the lady acquiesced, with the assurance that she should reward him in such a way that he would be satisfied.

After this, he asked for seventeen hand-picked kernels of incense, four consecrated wax tapers, eight ells of the best scarlet, a diamond, an emerald, a ruby, and a sapphire, jewels which a woman would be apt to wear around her neck both before and after she was married; secondly, he should be closed or locked up alone in the cellar, and the key kept by the lady herself, so that she would be well assured in regard to her jewelry and her scarlet, while he would be undisturbed and unmolested till he had succeeded in raising the treasure. Hereupon he and the drummer were given a meal, and he, the drummer, a gratuity for interpreting. In the meantime, the desired objects were fetched, and then Hopalong was locked up in the cellar, from which it seemed impossible for a body to escape, for the window, or cellar hole, which faced the street, was high up and on top of that well secured by the aforementioned iron grating. The interpreter, however, was dismissed and straightway came to me and reported the whole course of events.

6. *sign of the Hedgehog*] scholars seem to agree that Hopalong probably means the sign of Scorpio.

Neither Hopalong nor myself wasted time sleeping when other people are wont to sleep the soundest, but rather, after I had broken away the grating as easily as a piece of cheese, I let a rope down into the cellar to my Hopalong and by means of this pulled him up to me, together with all the plunder, among which I found the beautiful emerald I had demanded.

The booty did not gladden my heart nearly as much as the roguish trick in which I had succeeded so well. The drummer had left the city the evening before, but the day after the successful raising of the treasure my Hopalong was strolling about the city, in the company of others who were marveling at the cunning thief, at the very time when they were making arrangements at the city gates to catch him. And now look you, Simplice, this is the way your Hopalong's dexterity was achieved and perfected by me. I am only telling you about this by way of example, for if I told you all the rascally and cunning tricks which he was obliged to carry out to please me, I would be willing to wager that the time would grow too long for you and me both, even though they are merry things. Indeed, if one were to describe everything, as you described your tomfooleries, it would make a far thicker and far merrier book than your whole biography; but I will tell you just one more little thing.

Chapter 20

How Hopalong and Courage robbed two Italians

When we saw that we should be obliged to remain for some time yet before Casale we not only lived in tents, but quite a few built huts from other materials, to try and manage that much better during the lengthy stay. Among other hucksters there were two from Milan in camp; they had constructed a hut out of boards to keep their wares that much safer, which wares consisted of shoes, boots, doublets, shirts, and all kinds of other clothes, both for officers and common soldiers of foot and horse. These two were causing me much loss and harm, to my mind, namely by buying from the army people all kinds of silverware and jewels for half or even a fourth of their value, which profit should have been mine if it had not been for them. Now for this I thought to pay them a little interest, since I did not have the power to stop them completely in their business dealings.

Downstairs in the hut was a storeroom for their wares, and this was also their shop; their resting place where they slept, however, was above, under the roof. A ladder of about seven rungs led up to it, and they had left a hole in the floor, not only to hear the better when and if thieves were breaking in to rob them, but also to welcome such thieves with pistols, with which they were well provided. Now when I saw for myself how the door could be opened without making any particular noise I easily made my plans. My Hopalong was obliged to furnish me with a bundle of sharp thorns which was the length of a man and which also it almost took a man to carry, and I filled a brass syringe which held a good measure with sharp vinegar. Thus equipped, we both went to said hut when everyone was fast asleep. To open the door quietly was no great trick for me, because earlier I had inspected everything carefully; and when this had been accomplished and done, Hopalong fastened the bundle of thorns at the foot of the ladder, which did not have a door in front of it, which noise awakened both Italians so that they began to stir. We could well imagine that they would first look down through the hole above, which actually happened; but I straightway squirted the eyes of one of them so full of vinegar that he lost his foresightedness in an instant; but the other one ran down the ladder in his shirt and sleeping drawers and was received so unkindly by the bundle of thorns that he too, like his companion, could not but imagine at such an unforeseen turn of affairs and in his great fright that he was dealing with pure sorcery and demonic specters. In the meantime Hopalong had snatched up a dozen troopers' doublets and made off with them; but I was satisfied with a piece of linen and with that turned my back and clapped the door shut behind me, leaving the two Italians in their affliction, which no doubt left the one still wiping his eyes and the other having to deal with his bundle of thorns.

Look you, Simplice, that's what I was capable of, and that's how I trained Hopalong, by and by. I did not steal, as you have heard, out of need or want, but mostly because I wished to avenge myself on my adversaries; but Hopalong, in the meantime, learned the art so well and became such a master at such tricks that he would have ventured to steal anything unless it were tied with chains to God's own heaven above. And I gladly let him enjoy what he stole, for I did not grudge him a purse of his own, but permitted him to do and deal as he pleased with half of the stolen goods (since we divided such booty between us). But because he was very intent on gambling he rarely built up a large sum of money, and though at times he got together the beginnings of a considerable sum, he did not long keep it in his possession, since every time fickle fortune, in the form of the fickle dice, snatched the foundation of wealth from him. Otherwise he remained completely true and obedient to me, so that I should not have ventured to find a better slave in the whole world. Now hear further what he earned by that, how I rewarded him, and how I finally separated from him.

Chapter 21

Tale of a battle which took place during sleep

Some time earlier, before Mantua[1] was taken by our side, our regiment was obliged to leave Casale and join the siege of Mantua; there more water ran over my mill than in the previous camp, for since there were more soldiers there, especially Germans, I also had more customers and more work from them, by which my pile of money increased at a noticeably more rapid rate, so that several times I sent bills of exchange to Prague and to cities elsewhere in the German Empire, during which happy state of prosperity, great daily profit, and sufficient abundance which I and my rabble were enjoying while many another was obliged to suffer hunger and want, my Hopalong began to play the nobleman. He wished to make it his daily habit to do nothing but eat and drink, gamble and strut about, and to loll in the lap of indolence, and of course he let the sutler's business lie fallow and opportunities to snatch something or other go unheeded; on top of this, he also had attached to himself a few depraved and prodigal companions who led him astray and made him unfit for everything I had taken him in and trained him for in all sorts of ways.

"Hah!" they said, "Are you a man and let your whore be master over both yourself and what is yours? It would be bad enough if you had a shrewish wife and were obliged to suffer that kind of thing from her. If I were in your shoes, I'd beat her till she obeyed me or, by the devil, chase her off, &c."

All this I heard in time, with great indignation and vexation, and pondered on ways and means to make my Hopalong hop along without letting any of this be noticed by him and his fine friends. My rabble

1. *Mantua*] on July 18, 1630.

(among which I counted four strong lads as servants) was loyal to me and on my side; the officers of the regiment were not unfavorably disposed towards me, the colonel himself wishing me well and the colonel's lady even more so, and with gifts I put under obligation to me even more everyone I believed would be of assistance to me in this future civil war which I was sure Hopalong would declare on me presently.

I well knew that the husband, which Hopalong, however, was obliged to represent only *pro forma*, was acting as the head of my sutlery and that I plied my trade under the cover of his person, and that I should soon lose the sutlery if I lacked such a figurehead; therefore I proceeded most cautiously. Every day I gave him money both to gamble and to feast with, not that I wished to assure the constancy of his former behavior, but to make him that much more self-confident, insolent, and unrestrained towards me, so that as a consequence he should pull off a really foolish trick, and by a truly brutish act show himself unworthy of me and mine, in a word, that he should give me cause to divorce him; for I had already earned and scraped together and also put into safekeeping elsewhere so much that I no longer felt much concern for him or the sutlery, indeed, for the whole war and what I might yet get and gain from it.

But I know not whether Hopalong did not have the heart to follow the advice of his companions to openly demand of me authority over everything, or whether he was just heedlessly continuing in his above-described slothful ways. For he acted quite friendly and humble and never gave me a sour look, much less a harsh word. I well knew of the plan to which his companions had inveigled him. But from his actions I could not see that he was actually thinking of daring to undertake anything of the sort against me; however, it finally came about in a wondrous way that he offended me, with the result that he and I then came to a parting of the ways, whether he liked it or not.

Once I was lying beside him, sleeping without a care in the world, after he had just returned home drunk. Look you, all of a sudden, with all his might, he struck me in the face, so that I was not only awakened by it, but indeed so that the blood spurted profusely from my nose and mouth, and my head was spinning so from this blow that I still wonder that it did not knock all my teeth down my throat. Now anyone can well consider and imagine what a pious litany I sang him: I called him a murderer and whatever other such pretty titles came to my lips.

He, for his part, said: "You son of a b., why don't you let me have my money? For sure I won it fair and square!" and was about to deal me further blows, so that I had great trouble fending them off, with the result that we both came to sit up in bed and began to wrestle with each other, as it were. And because he kept on and on demanding money from me, I gave him a good clout aside the ear, which put him back to sleep; I, however, whisked out of the tent and started to wail so loudly that not only my mother and the rest of the rabble but also our neighbors were awakened by it and crawled out of their tents and huts to see what was to be done or what had happened anyway. All these were persons from the staff who are generally quartered behind the lines with the sutlers, namely the chaplain, the regimental clerk, the regimental quartermaster, the provost, the hangman, the whores' sergeant,[2] and the like. To them I told my sad tale of woe, and my appearance did indeed confirm in what manner my fine husband had treated me, without guilt and cause: My heaving white bosom was all bespattered with blood, and my face, which had never before been observed except full of most enticing loveliness, Hopalong's merciless fist had changed so horribly with a single blow that no one knew Courage by anything except her piteous voice, in spite of the fact that no one there had ever heard her complain before. I was asked the cause of our discord and the battle resulting from it. Now when I told

2. *whores' sergeant*] the officer in charge of all the women and boys who accompanied the baggage train. The following remark is found in Leonhard Fronsperger's *Kriegszbuch*: "Item, for this post an old and experienced soldier is chosen and used, for in his power and under his command is the whole baggage train [*Tross*] as well as whores and boys [*Buben*]."

Jra.

11. Anger. From *The Seven Deadly Sins.* 1619

everything that had happened, everyone standing about thought that Hopalong must have gone mad; but I believed he had started this whole play at the instigation of his friends and drinking companions, first to get the trousers away from me, secondly to get authority over everything, and lastly to get hold of all my money.

Now while we were thus babbling with each other and several women were undertaking to stanch the bleeding, Hopalong himself scrambled out of our tent. He walked over to us by the watchfire, which was burning near the colonel's baggage, and could scarce find and utter words enough to beg pardon of me and everyone else for the mistake he had made; a little more, and he would have fallen on his knees before me to receive forgiveness from me again and to be taken back into his former state of grace and favor; but I stopped my ears and did not wish to see or hear him, till finally our lieutenant colonel came up, having made the rounds, to whom he offered to swear a solemn oath that he had dreamed he had been sitting at the gaming table, where someone had attempted to cheat him out of a considerable stake, which person he had then struck a blow, but instead had unwillingly and unintentionally hit his dear innocent wife, while they were sleeping. The lieutenant colonel was a gentleman who hated me and all whores like the plague, but on the other hand was not wholly ill-disposed towards my Hopalong; therefore he told me to betake myself straightway back to the tent and shut my mouth, or he would hand me over to the provost and might even have me whipped out of camp, which I had long since deserved.

"Hell and damnation! That is a harsh sentence. Spare me such judges," I thought to myself. "But it hardly matters; even if you are a lieutenant colonel and impervious to both my beauty and my bribes, there are others, and indeed more than of your kind, who are willing to be beguiled by them into siding with me." I kept as quiet as a mouse, but my Hopalong did too, when he told him that if he should come before him again he would punish him at one time by day for what he then would have done to me two times by night, so that he would surely not come before him a third time. Both of us together he told to make peace before the sun rose, so that this coming morning he would have no reason to turn us over to a mediator, whose *procedere* would surely give us good reason to scratch our heads.

So we went back to bed together, each with his pains, for I had dealt blows as liberally to Hopalong as he had to me. He kept assuring me with mighty oaths that he had really had a dream, but I maintained that all dreams were false, whereas the punch in the face I had gotten had been real enough. He wished to show by deeds his love for me, but the prank he had played, or rather, the fact that I should have liked to be rid of him, deprived him of any of my favors. Indeed, the next day I not only did not give him any more money for gambling, but not even any for drinking, and even less kind words; and so that he would not get at the money which I still had with me to run our business, I hid it on my mother, who was obliged to carry it on her person day and night, sewn into her shift.

Chapter 22

For what reasons Hopalong and Courage separated, and what she gave him as a parting gift

Straightway after this nocturnal battle of ours, only a little time passed till Mantua was taken by a clever stratagem; indeed, the peace itself between the Imperial army in Italy and the French, between the Dukes of Savoy and Nevers,[1] followed shortly hereafter, almost as if the Italian war must needs end with our own encounter. And for just that reason the French left Savoy and stormed back to France and the Imperial armies to Germany, to see what the Swede was doing, and I was obliged to move along with them as well, just as if I had been a soldier myself. We were quartered with our regiment for a few weeks near a place in the Imperial fiefs near the Danube, in an open field, either to recuperate or because the bloody dysentery and the plague were rampant among our troops; there I did not enjoy by far the same comforts as in noble Italy. But I made do as best I could and even made peace again with my Hopalong (since he was showing such doglike humility towards me), but only *pro forma*, for I was waiting daily for an opportunity to rid myself of him.

This fervent wish was granted me in the following way, which proves sufficiently that a cautious, reasonable, indeed innocent man, who waking and sober cannot be harmed either by woman, world, or the devil himself, can very easily fall into misery and misfortune and lose all his wealth and health through his own silly frailty when he is stupified by sleep or wine.

Now just as I was in humor most vengeful and implacable if I were given the slightest insult or thought injustice had been done me, just so

1. *peace . . . Nevers*] in 1631.

my body, if it were only the least bit hurt, proved incurable, as it were; I know not whether it was imitating my humor or whether the tenderness of my skin and my peculiar complexion could not bear such hard blows as a Salzburg peasant can. Once, when I still bore on my tender face the black and blue marks and other testimonials to Hopalong's fist, with which he had hit me in the camp before Mantua, and while, in the aforementioned camp on the Danube, I was again lying in a sound sleep, he grasped me about the middle, took me on his shoulder, and, with me in my shift, just as he had caught me, he ran towards the colonel's watchfire and to all appearances intended to throw me into it. I, for my part, when I awoke, did not know what was happening to me, but nevertheless sensed the danger, since I was completely naked and Hopalong was running with me so quickly towards the fire; therefore I began to scream as if I had fallen among assassins. From this everyone awoke, indeed the colonel himself sprang from his tent with his lance, and also the other officers came, thinking to quell a riot (for at that time we had nothing at all to fear from the enemy), but they found nothing but a pretty, albeit ridiculous sight and a foolish spectacle. I truly believe that it must have been right agreeable and amusing to behold. The watch caught Hopalong with his un-willing and screaming burden before he was able to throw it into the fire; and when they saw that it was naked and recognized it to be his Courage, the corporal was honorable enough to throw a cloak around my body. In the meantime there gathered around us a crowd of officers, both high and low, who were nearly dying of laughter and who were joined not only by the colonel himself but also by the lieutenant colonel who had only recently made peace between me and Hopalong by threatening us.

When, in the meantime, Hopalong of a sudden acted rational again (I myself know not at all what really was in his heart), or when he had once more come to his senses, the colonel asked him what he meant by this cavalry charge. Then he answered that he had dreamed his Courage had been all covered over and surrounded by snakes, wherefore he had

Auaritia.

12. Avarice. From *The Seven Deadly Sins.* 1619

had the idea that the best thing to do to save her and free her of them was to carry her to either fire or water, and had therefore grasped her to that end, and, as they had all seen, had carried her here, for which action he was more than sorry, to the bottom of his heart. But both the colonel himself and the lieutenant colonel who had taken his side at Mantua shook their heads at this, and because everyone had already had his fill of laughing, they had him taken to the provost for the time being, but they sent me to my tent to sleep out the night.

The following morning our trial began, and it was to end straightway too, because they do not generally last very long during wartime, as they do in some places in peacetime. Everyone knew all along that I was not really Hopalong's lawful wedded wife but only his concubine, and therefore we did not need to go before a *consistorium*[2] to get a divorce, which I demanded because my life was not safe with him in the same bed with me; and for this very reason I had the approbation of nearly all the *assessoribus*,[3] who held that for such a cause even a real marriage could be dissolved. The lieutenant colonel, who before Mantua had been completely on Hopalong's side, was now completely against him, and nearly all the rest of the regiment was on my side. After I had produced our written contract, which showed how we had promised each other to live together till we were legally wed, and particularly since I knew how to exploit and exaggerate the danger to life and limb which I should have to fear in the future from such a husband, the decision was that on threat of certain punishment we were to separate, yet arrange together to divide what we had gained and gotten together. To this I replied that the latter was contrary to the agreement by which we were first joined together and that Hopalong, since he had had me with him, or to speak more plainly, since I had taken him unto me and established my sutlery, had wasted more than he had won, which indeed I could show and prove by the testimony

2. *consistorium*] a diocesan court with jurisdiction in matters (as of marriage and titles) relating to general ecclesiastical and moral discipline.
3. *assessoribus*] lawyers.

of the whole regiment. Finally it was decreed that if an agreement with reasonable concern for these circumstances could not be reached amicably by the two of us together, then the regiment would have the final decision on the basis of the evidence.

I was more than satisfied with this decision, and Hopalong himself was content to be satisfied with very little; for because I no longer treated him or my rabble as well as I had in Italy, on account of the diminished profits, so that it seemed as if the wolf were scratching at the door, the conceited ass thought that matters were going downhill with me in regard to money and that I had far less than was actually the case and of which he knew nothing. And it was fair that he did not know about it, for he also did not know why I so stubbornly held back with it.

Just at that time, Simplice, the regiment of dragoons at Soest[4] under which you were probably learning your ABC's was reinforced by all kinds of young lads who were to be found here and there serving officers of the regiments of foot and who had now grown to manhood but did not wish to become musketeers; this was a good opportunity for Hopalong, for which reason he was quite willing to come to that much more satisfactory an agreement with me, which indeed we arrived at together on our own: I gave him the best horse I had, along with saddle and tack, *item* one hundred ducats in cash and the dozen troopers' doublets which he had stolen in Italy at my instigation; for till now we had not dared let them be seen in our possession. At the same time it was agreed that he would buy from me for one crown my *Spiritus famil.*,[5] which indeed happened. And in this manner I dismissed and endowed Hopalong. Now you shall presently hear too with what manner of fine gift I blessed you yourself and how I rewarded your folly at Sauerbrunnen. Just be patient and hear first how Hopalong fared with his thing in the glass flask.

4. *Soest*] See *Simplicissimus*, Book II, Chapters 33 ff.
5. *Spiritus famil.*] had to be sold for one crown less than it had been bought for, thus Hopalong is in great danger of landing in hell.

As soon as he had it he got bees in his bonnet. If he but looked at a fellow who never in his life had done him the least bit of harm, he straightway wished to challenge him, and he was the victor in all his duels too. He was able to find all hidden treasures and other secret matters which need not be mentioned here. But after he found out what a dangerous guest he was harboring he sought to get rid of it; yet he could not sell it again because the sale price could not be lowered. Now rather than lose his own skin he thought to give it back and hang it on me and so threw it at my feet when we met again at the general rendezvous before marching on Regensburg. But I merely laughed at him, and not for nothing either, for not only did I not pick it up, but when Hopalong got back to his own billet he found it back in his pocket again. I have been told that he threw the piece of trash into the Danube several times, but every time he found it in his pocket once more, till he finally threw it into an oven and got rid of it that way. Now while he was thus being plagued by it I became quite ill at ease at this business; therefore I turned all I owned into silver, dismissed my servants, and traveled to Passau with my Bohemian mother, to await the end of the war while living on my considerable money, particularly since I had good cause to fear that I should have to stand trial as a sorceress if Hopalong were to lodge a complaint against me because of the sale and resale of the thing.

Chapter 23

How Courage once more lost a husband, and how she conducted herself after that

In Passau I did not fare as well by far as I had expected; it was much too priestly and pious for me: I should have preferred to see soldiers there instead of nuns, and a few courtiers instead of monks. Nevertheless, I stayed there, because at that time not only Bohemia but almost all of the provinces of Germany were overrun with war. Now when I observed that everyone there seemed to be devoted to the service of God, I likewise accommodated myself, at least outwardly, to their ways and customs, and what is more, my Bohemian mother, or nurse, had the great good fortune to go the way of all flesh in the splendor of her assumed godliness and in this pious place, and I therefore had her buried with more splendor than if she had died in Prague at St. James Gate. I took it to be an omen of future misery for me, for now I had no one in the world to whom I could have entrusted completely my person and my property; and therefore I hated the innocent place in which I had been robbed of my best friend, nurse, and teacher; however, I stayed there patiently till I received news that Wallenstein had taken Prague,[1] the capital of my homeland, and had once more put it under the rule of the Emperor; for upon receiving this news, I went back to said Prague, where I had most of my money in safekeeping, because the Swede was ruling in Munich[2] and in all of Bavaria, and particularly since in Passau there was great fear of him.

But hardly had I made my nest there—indeed, I had not even settled

1. *Wallenstein . . . Prague*] on May 4, 1632.
2. *Swede . . . Munich*] Gustavus Adolphus, King of Sweden, entered Munich on May 17, 1632.

down to enjoy my hard-earned money and property in peace and luxury, so I thought, in this city, which was large and, so I believed, very safe—when, look you, Arnim[3] defeated the Imperial troops at Liegnitz, and after he had taken fifty-three cavalry squadrons there, he came to threaten Prague. But the Most Illustrious Ferdinand III (while he himself was laying siege to Regensburg)[4] sent Gallas to the aid of this, his own city, through which succor the enemy was forced to leave once more not only Prague but all of Bohemia.

At that time I saw that neither the great powerful cities nor their ramparts, towers, walls, and moats could protect me or my property from the armed might of those who lodge only under the open sky, in huts and tents, and rove from one place to the next; therefore I sought to attach myself once more to such an army.

I was still fairly sleek and attractive at that time, though no longer as beautiful by far as a few years before. Nevertheless, my industry and experience got me from Gallas' support troops another captain of infantry who wed me, almost as if it were the duty or otherwise peculiar talent of the city of Prague to provide me with husbands, and in particular captains of infantry. Our wedding was as splendid as a count's, and hardly was it over when we received orders to proceed to the Imperial army before Nördlingen, which had shortly before joined with the Spanish Cardinal-Infante Ferdinand, had taken Donauwörth, and was besieging Nördlingen.[5] Now the Prince of Weimar and Gustavus Horn came to succor the city, whereupon there ensued a bloody battle, the events and consequences of which will not be forgotten for as long as the world shall stand. But whereas the battle turned out well for our side, it turned out ill, even harmful, for me alone, as it were, because I was robbed of my husband in the first attack, before he had yet quite warmed my bed; on top of this, I did

3. *Arnim*] Johann Georg von Arnim (1581–1641), leader of the Saxon army.

4. *Regensburg*] besieged from May 15 to July 17, 1634.

5. *Nördlingen*] had been besieged since August 18, 1634. The battle of Nördlingen, in which the Imperial troops defeated Bernhard of Saxe-Weimar and Marshal Horn, took place on September 6, 1634.

not have the good fortune, as in other earlier battles, to win any booty for myself and by my own hand, because others got there before I did, and also because I could not get into battle because of my husband's untimely death. All this I judged to be a sure prophecy of my future ruin, which caused the first attack of melancholia which I really experienced in all my days.

After the encounter, the victorious army separated into various groups to take back the lost German provinces, which, however, were more ruined than retaken and occupied. With the regiment under which my husband had served, I followed the corpo which conquered the region around the Lake of Constance and Württemberg, and then I seized the opportunity to go to the homeland of my first captain of infantry (who earlier had also been Prague's gift to me, but whom Hoya had taken away from me again) and to look to his inheritance, which *patrimonium*, together with the location of the town, pleased me so much that I straightway chose this Imperial city[6] as my residence, mainly because the foes of the Imperial House of Austria had been in part dispersed and chased across the Rhine and elsewhere, I know not whither, so that I could imagine nothing more certain than that I should be able to live there safely for the rest of my life. Anyway, I did not wish to go back to war, because after the famous battle of Nörd-lingen everything had been looted everywhere to such an extent that the Imperial side could hope, so I suspected, for little real booty.

Therefore I began to keep house like a proper countryman: I bought livestock and property, I hired farmhands and maids, and acted just as if the war had indeed ended with this battle, or at least as if a peace treaty had already actually been signed; and to this end I had all my money, which I had in safekeeping in Prague and in other large cities, sent to me and used most of it for this. And now look you, Simplice, according to my reckoning and your biography, we both made fools of ourselves at one and the same time, I in Suabia and you in Hanau.

6. *Imperial city*] presumably Offenburg in Baden was where Courage settled down.

I squandered my money, but you squandered your youth; you went to a bad war, while I vainly imagined a time of peace which still lay far off in the future. For before I had rightly taken root, there came troops marching through and there was billeting, which by no means eased the oppressive *contributiones*; and if my money had not been pretty plentiful, or if I had not had wits enough to wisely conceal the fact that I had it, I should have been ruined soon enough. For no one in the city bore me any good will, not even my late husband's relatives, because I was enjoying the property which he had left behind and which would otherwise have fallen to them, if, as they said, an ill wind had not blown me into town. Therefore I had heavy levies imposed on me and was nevertheless not spared having troops billeted with me either. In other words, I fared just like any widow who is forsaken by everyone.

But this I am not telling you to complain, nor do I desire solace, help or compassion from you, but I am telling you this so that you shall know that it still did not worry or sadden me very much, but even made me happy when we were obliged to provide winter quarters for a regiment; for as soon as that happened, I began to play up to the officers. There was nothing but eating and drinking, whores and rascals, in my house; I behaved as they wished, and they in turn, once they had swallowed the bait, were obliged to behave as I wished, so that they carried but little money out of winter quarters back into the field; to which end I then played more than a thousand different tricks, and despite anyone who at that time would have opposed me. At all times I kept a few maids who were not a hair better than myself, but proceeded so cautiously, wisely, and prudently that even the magistrate itself, my then beloved city fathers, had more cause to look the other way than to punish me, particularly since the longer I was there to cast my nets, the longer their wives and daughters would remain virtuous.

This life I led for several years before I came a cropper. Every year, towards summer, when Mars once more returned to the field of battle, I took inventory and settled my accounts, to find out what the war had cost me the preceding winter, at which time I generally found that my wealth and profits far surpassed the amounts levied upon me. But, Simplice, now it is high time I told you what kind of leach I tanned your hide with; therefore I shall henceforth address not you but the Reader; but of course you may listen all you wish and not hesitate to interrupt if you should think I am lying.

Chapter 24

How Simplicissimus and Courage became acquainted and cheated each other

We were obliged to endure a billet of many troops in our city when the Bavarian, French, and Weimar forces were scuffling and snapping at each other inside the Suabian borders. Among these, most of the officers had a great taste for what I was willing to serve them for a fee; when both because of my great greed for the money which I was once more earning in this way and because of my insatiable nature I went much too far and began to serve almost indiscriminately anyone who wished it, look you, then I got what I had by rights deserved twelve or fifteen years ago, namely the dear French disease,[1] with kindest regards. This broke out and began to decorate me with rubies just as merry and joyous springtime was beginning to bedizen the whole earth with all kinds of beautiful and highly decorative flowers. It was my good fortune that I had the means to have myself cured of it, which cure then took place in a town by the Lake of Constance. But because, according to my *medici* statement, my blood was not yet completely purified, he advised me to take the Sauerbrunnen cure and thereby regain my former health that much more completely. In consequence, I fitted myself out most elegantly with a beautiful carriage, two horses, a servant, and a maid who was cut of the same cloth as I, except that she had not yet suffered from the above-mentioned gay disease.

I had been in Sauerbrunnen hardly a week when Master Simplicius made my acquaintance, for like will to like, as the devil said to the collier. I conducted myself very nobly, and because Simplicius made such a show and had many servants, I took him to be a proper

1. *the dear French disease*] *morbus gallicus*, syphilis.

nobleman and pondered whether I might throw my rope over his horns and make him my husband (as I had already done frequently with others). And he came sailing into the dangerous port of my insatiable lusts under full sail and before a strong wind, just as I had wished, and I treated him like Circe did the erring *Ulissem*; and soon I was confident for sure I had him safely in my net, but the tricky bird tore a hole in it with a pretty little trick, by which he showed his great ingratitude, ridiculing me and ultimately harming himself. By shooting blanks from a pistol and using a water-squirt full of blood in *secret*, he made me believe that I had been wounded, so that I was viewed, front and behind, not only by the leech who was supposed to bandage me, but also by almost all the people in Sauerbrunnen, who afterwards pointed their fingers at me, sang a song about it, and mocked me in such fashion that I was no longer able to bear the ridicule, but quit Sauerbrunnen and the spa before my cure was completed.

That booby Simplex calls me wanton in his biography, in Book V, Chapter vi, *item* when he says I was more *mobilis* than *nobilis*. I admit to both; but if he had himself been noble, or if there had been a decent bone in his body, then he would not have tangled with a baggage as wanton and as brazen as he took me to be, much less proclaimed and spread abroad to all the world, as he did, his dishonor and my shame. Dear Reader! What honor and fame is it for him now, that he (to use his own words) quickly gained entrance to her house and all favors which he might wish and desire from a woman whose wantonness he came to abhor? Indeed, from one who had but recently recuperated from the wood cure?[2] The poor devil certainly has won tremendous honor from bragging about what he might better and with greater honor have concealed. But that is the way it goes with these studs, who, like ignorant beasts, chase after anything in skirts, like a hunter does after any kind of game. He says I was sleek; he should know,

2. *wood cure*] a cure for syphilis requiring the patient to fast, sweat as much as possible, and drink only decoctions made by boiling various kinds of wood in water.

however, that at that time I no longer had even the seventeenth part of my former beauty, but was already gilding the lily with all kinds of paint and rouge, of which he himself licked off no small amount, but indeed a great deal. But enough of this; fools should be groomed with clubs. But that was nothing; now let the Reader hear how I finally paid him back.

I left Sauerbrunnen in great vexation and anger, pondering on revenge, because I had been both insulted and scorned by Simplicio. And my maid had been just as busy at Sauerbrunnen as I, and (because the poor ninny could not take a joke) she had been left with a baby boy instead of the usual fee, which child she brought safely into the world on my farm outside town. She was obliged to have it baptized "Simplicius," though Simplicius had never in all his life laid a finger on her.[3] Now as soon as I found out that Simplicius had married a farmer's daughter, my maid was obliged to wean her child, and after I had fitted it out with soft diapers, indeed with silken blankets and swaddling bands, to make my deceit more complete and decorous, she, in the company of my farmhand, was obliged to take it to Simplicii house, where she left it by night on his doorstep, with a written note that he had begot it with me. No one can believe how this deception delighted me, particularly when I heard that he was so well punished by his magistrate because of it and that his wife served him my pretty little trick every day with horseradish and mustard, *item* that I succeeded in making the simpleton really believe that I, a barren woman, had born a child, when if I had been of that kind I should surely not have waited for him, but should have accomplished in my youth what he thought I had done when I was approaching old age; for at that time I had seen at least forty years and was not worthy of such a rascal as Simplicius was.

3. *finger on her*] cf. Appendix B, page 191.

Chapter 25

Courage is caught at her evil deeds and driven out of the city

Now I should really break off and stop telling the story of my further life, because it has been made amply clear what kind of lady Simplicius bragged of having duped; but just as all which has already been told will no doubt bring him nothing but scorn and dishonor, so there will be just as little honor for him in what I shall now tell.

I had behind my house in town a garden with fruit trees, herbs, and flowers which could compare and vie with any other, and next to me lived an old *moechaberis*,[1] or Susannah man,[2] who had a wife who was much older than himself. He soon discovered of what ilk I was, and I did not refuse to make use of his assistance in time of need, wherefore we then often came together[3] in said garden and in the greatest haste and like thieves, as it were, broke flowers, so that his jealous old wife would not notice it, and we were actually nowhere safer, so we thought, than in this garden, with its greenery and covered walks, which covered our shame and vice from the eyes of mankind but not from the eyes of God. Moral people will object that our measure of sin must have either been brimming full or running over, else God in his everlasting mercy would have been willing to lead us to repentance and correction.

In the beginning of *Septembris* we had made a *rendez-vous* to meet that same lovely evening in the garden under a pear tree, just as two musketeers from the town's garrison had laid plans that same evening to steal their share of my pears, and indeed had climbed the tree and

1. *moechaberis*] from the Latin *moechator*, adulterer.
2. *Susannah man*] one who behaves like the elders in the Biblical story of Susanna and the Elders.
3. *came together*] this "pearquake" episode occurs in several anecdotes; cf. Antoine de la Sale, *Cent nouvelles nouvelle* (No. 46).

begun their harvest before I or the old lecher had come into the garden. It was pretty dark, and my lover arrived before I did, but before long I was there too and began with him that work which we were wont to accomplish together. By Amor! I know not how it happened, but one of the soldiers moved in the tree to better observe our antics and was so careless as to spill all the pears he had picked; and when these fell to the ground I and the old man could not but imagine that it was a violent earthquake, sent and invoked by God to frighten us from our shameful sinning, as we indeed gave each other to understand in so many words, parting from each other in fear and terror. But those in the tree could not stifle their laughter, which caused us even greater terror, particularly the old man, who then thought it was a ghost who was plaguing us. Therefore we each went to his own house.

The next day I had hardly reached the market place when one musketeer shouted: "I know something!" Another asked at the top of his lungs: "Well, what do you know?" The first answered: "Last night we had a pearquake!" The longer this clamor lasted, the louder it became, so that I straightway knew which way the wind was blowing and became red in the face, though I was generally not wont to feel ashamed. I straightway reckoned that I had quite a few odds against me, but not that it would get as bad as it actually did. For after even the children in the streets were telling our tale, the magistrate could do nothing but lay hold of me and the old man and have each of us put into prison. But we both denied everything as stubbornly as witches, even though they threatened us with hangman and torture.

Inventory was made of my property, which was then put under lock and seal. My servants were examined under oath, but their testimony was contradictory because not all of them knew of my whorish capers, and the maids were loyal to me. Finally I botched things up myself, because the chief magistrate, who called me "dear cousin" and frequently came to the prison and feigned great pity, was in reality a greater friend of justice than any cousin of mine. For when he persuaded me with completely false friendliness that my old swain had confessed to committing adultery with me, not once but repeatedly, I blurted out: "May the devil fill his trap with pitch, that he could not keep it shut, the old shit!" and then begged my alleged friend that he should loyally help me out of my trouble. But he, for his part, gave me a harsh sermon, opened the door, and showed me a notary and witnesses, all of whom had heard and recorded everything he and I had said to each other.

Thereupon strange things began to happen: Most of the councilmen held that I should be put to torture, because I would no doubt confess to more such capers, and that then, on the basis of the evidence, I should be made a head shorter, because I was a useless encumbrance upon this good earth, of which sentence I was duly notified. I, on the other hand, allowed that they were not so much seeking to satisfy justice and act according to the laws as they were anxious to confiscate my money and property. If they were to proceed with me that harshly, then many others who were held to be respectable citizens would needs keep me company and go to the grave with me. I could talk like a lawyer, and my arguments and *protestationes* were so sharp and sly that even the experts were shocked. Finally it happened that I was forced to quit the city, under oath to keep the peace and not return, leaving behind as a more than well deserved punishment all my *mobilia* and property, among which was more than one thousand sovereigns in cash. My clothes and what I carried on my person were left me, except for a few jewels which had stuck to this or that palm. *In summa*, what was I to do? I should have merited much worse if they had wished to proceed more strictly with me, but it was wartime, after all, and every man thanked merciful heaven (I should have said "every woman") that the town *taliter qualiter*[4] had thus rid itself of me.

4. *taliter qualiter*] one way or the other.

Chapter 26

Courage becomes the wife of a musketeer and at the same time hawks tobacco and brandy; her husband is sent off as a courier, finds along the way a dead soldier whom he strips, and, because the breeches will not come off, hacks off his legs, packs everything together, seeks shelter with a peasant, leaves the legs behind during the night, and takes French leave, which leads to a right ridiculous farce

At that time no Imperial troops or armies, which I thought to join once more, were camped anywhere near by. Now because I lacked these and the troops of Weimar and Hesse were in the Kinzig Valley[1] and in the surrounding towns at that time, I planned to go to them to see if I might perhaps get a soldier for a husband once more. But, alas, the first bloom of my incomparable beauty had passed, wilted like a spring flower. And while my recent mishap and the grief it caused me had disfigured me not a little, I also had lost my wealth, which often helps old women to catch a husband. Of the clothes and the jewelry which had been left me I sold what was still worth money and got about two hundred guilders together; I set out with these and in the company of a courier to seek my fortune. But I met with nothing but misfortune, for before I reached Schiltach[2] we were caught by a party of Weimar musketeers who beat the courier, robbed him, and chased him off, and dragged me with them to their quarters. I passed myself off as an Imperial soldier's wife whose husband had been killed in Breisgau and persuaded the fellows that I had been in my husband's homeland, but that now I wished to go back to my home in the Alsace.

1. *Kinzig Valley*] in the Black Forest.
2. *Schiltach*] a city on the Kinzig.

At that time I was, as I said above, by far not so beautiful as before, but still of such constitution as to make a musketeer of the party fall so violently in love with me that he desired me for his wife. What should I or could I do? I should rather grant him with good grace what he sought out of love than be forced to grant the same thing to the entire party. *In summa*, I became a musketeer's wife before the chaplain married us. I had it in mind to follow the sutler's trade once more, as I had once with Hopalong, but my purse was too light to accomplish this. I also lacked my Bohemian mother, and anyway, I thought my husband much too slovenly and shiftless for such a business; however, I began to hawk tobacco and brandy, almost as if I meant to regain a penny at a time what I had recently lost by the thousands. It was sour work to march on foot that way and on top of that to carry a heavy pack, aside from the fact that there was often very little food or drink, in short, discomfort which I had never tried, much less become accustomed to. Finally I succeeded in acquiring an excellent mule which could not only carry great weights, but could also run faster than many a good horse. Now as soon as I had in this way acquired two mules, I cared for them most diligently, so that each could render its service that much better. Because now I as well as my baggage were being carried, I could afford to be more patient with my lot and went on living this way till Mercy[3] dealt us some heavy blows near Herbsthausen in the beginning of May. But before I continue to tell the rest of my life story, I wish first to tell the Reader a pretty little caper[4] which my then husband brought about unintentionally while we were still camped in the Kinzig Valley.

At his officers' suggestion and with my approval he agreed to dress in old rags and, with an axe on his shoulder, disguised as a poor homeless carpenter, to carry some letters to their destinations, to which no

3. *Mercy*] Franz Freiherr von Mercy (d. 1645), a general of the Bavarian army who defeated Turenne at Herbsthausen (a village near Mergentheim on the Tauber in Württemberg) on May 5, 1645.

4. *little caper*] the story of the fiendish calf is based on an old tale. It also appears in Bebel's *Facetiae*, "De quondam Histrione," p. 62a.

13. The Farm. From *Capricci*. 1618

one dared to go because the presence of Imperial troops in the vicinity made it unsafe. These letters concerned the joining of several armies and other war plans. At that time the terrible cold was freezing stone and bone together, as it were, so that I almost pitied my poor lamb on his journey; but it could not be otherwise, because a good piece of money was to be earned by it, and he did indeed carry out the business very well. But on his way, while taking short cuts well known to him, he found a dead body which doubtless must have once been an officer, because it had on a pair of scarlet breeches with silver galloons, which kind of uniform officers generally wore at that time; and the doublet, the boots, and the spurs were of the same quality as the breeches. He looked over his find but could not tell whether the fellow had frozen to death or had been slain by the folk in the Black Forest; but it was all the same to him how he had died. He liked the doublet so much that he took it off the body, and when he had it he got a hankering for the breeches; to get them he was first obliged to take off the boots; this too he succeeded in doing. But when he attempted to pull the breeches off, they would not come off, because moisture from the already decaying body had collected in both the lining and outer cloth down around the knees where at that time it was customary to tie the breechbands, and as a consequence the breeches were frozen to the man's legs there as solid as a rock. But he did not wish to leave these breeches behind, and because in his haste the fool saw no other way to free one from the other, he hacked off the legs of the *corpo* with his axe, packed everything—breeches, doublet and legs—together and found, along with his bundle, a hospitable peasant who let him spend the night behind the warm stove.

That same night, unfortunately, the peasant's cow calved, which same calf the maid carried into the room because of the great cold and laid by the stove on a half a sheaf of straw next to my husband. In the meantime, it was near daybreak, and my husband's captured breeches had thawed away from the legs; therefore he took off some of his rags and put on instead the doublet and the breeches (which he turned inside or wrong side out), left his old rags and the man's legs lying next to the calf, climbed out the window, and came safely back to our billet.

Early that morning the maid came back to look after the calf; but when she saw the two legs lying there, together with my husband's old rags and leather apron, and did not find my husband, she began to scream as if she had fallen among assassins. She ran out of the room and clapped the door shut behind her as if the devil himself were after her, from which noise not only the peasant but the whole neighborhood awoke and imagined that soldiers had arrived, wherefore some took to their heels and others prepared to fight. The peasant himself heard from the maid, who was trembling with fear and fright, the cause of her screaming, namely that the calf had eaten up the poor carpenter whom they had given shelter for the night except for his legs and had made such a terrible face at her that she believed it would have sprung on her too if she had not shaken the dust from her heels. The peasant wished to kill the calf with his pike, but his wife would not allow him to risk such danger or to go into the room, but persuaded him to petition the mayor for help. The latter immediately had the churchbells rung to assemble the whole community and to storm the house together, to exterminate this common enemy of the human race in time, before it grew up to be a cow. Now it was a pretty spectacle to behold, the wife handing her children and household things out through one window while the peasants peered into the other to view the terrible dragon together with the legs lying next to it, which seemed to them sufficient proof of a terrible ferocity. The mayor ordered them to attack the house and kill the gruesome wonder-beast, but each was wary for his own hide. Everyone said: "What will it profit my wife and children if I should die?" Finally, following the counsel of an old peasant, it was decided to burn down the house together with the calf, whose mother must have been covered by a monster or dragon, and to recompense the peasant from the community treasury and to help him build a new house. This work was undertaken with a right good will, for they consoled themselves with the thought that they could count on the thievish soldiers to burn it down eventually anyway.

This story made me believe that my husband would have excellent good fortune in such capers, because this had happened to him by accident; what may he not be capable of, I thought, once I train him like Hopalong? But the fool was much too asinine and miserable for it; anyway, he turned up dead shortly afterwards at the battle of Herbsthausen, because this kind of joke he could not take.

Chapter 27

After Courage's husband falls in battle and Courage herself escapes on her mule, she meets a band of gypsies whose lieutenant takes her to wife; she tells the fortune of a love-stricken young lady, steals all her jewels at the same time, but does not keep them long, but rather must return them after a good beating

In the above-mentioned encounter I escaped on my good mule, after I had first thrown my tent and my least valuable baggage away, and retreated with the rest of the army, just as did Turenne,[1] almost as far as Cassel; and since my husband had fallen and I had no one any more whom I would have liked to take up with or who would have taken me to him, I took refuge with the gypsies who had formerly been with the Swedish main army but were now attached to Königsmark's[2] troops, who joined us near the Wartburg[3] and among whom I found a lieutenant who discerned in me good qualities and great skill in stealing, as well as some money and certain other virtues which these people find useful; look you, thus I straightway became his wife and had the advantage that I no longer needed either *oleum talci* or other things to smear my skin with to make it white and beautiful, because my station as well as my husband demanded of me that *couleur* which one commonly calls the devil's own. Therefore I began to besmear myself zealously with goosefat, louse salve, and other hair-dying tinctures so that in a short time I looked as hellish black as if I had been born in the middle of Egypt. Often I could not but laugh at myself and be

1. *Turenne*] Henri de La Tour d'Auvergne, Vicomte de Turenne (1611–1675), French general, fled to Cassel after losing the battle of Herbsthausen.

2. *Königsmark*] Johann Christoph Könisgsmark (1600–1633), a Swedish general.

3. *Wartburg*] probably the fortress in Thuringia, not the one of the same name in Franconia.

astonished at the many changes which I had undergone. Nevertheless, the life of a gypsy suited my humor so well that I should not have changed places even with a colonel's lady. In a short time I learned from an old Egyptian grandmother how to tell fortunes; I already knew how to lie and steal, except that I did not yet know the gypsies' own pretty tricks. But why make a fuss about it? I was soon so perfect that I could have passed for the generalissimo of all gypsy hags.

But still, I was not so clever that I should be everywhere safe from danger, indeed from painful blows, though I raked in more and brought my husband more to squander than any ten other gypsy women. Listen to how I once failed. On a march we were camped for a night and a day not far from a friendly city, and everyone had permission to enter the town to buy what he wished. I went to town too, more to steal and earn than to spend money or to buy anything, because I did not intend to acquire anything but what I could trade for with my five fingers or with some artful trick. I had not gotten far into the city when a *mademoiselle* sent her maid to me to tell me I should come and tell her young lady's fortune; from this messenger I learned in a round-about, offhand way, as if by accident, that the young lady's lover had rebelled and had forsaken her for another. Now I made good use of this; for when I came to the young lady, the fortune I told her hit the mark so nicely that in the opinion of the suffering *mademoiselle* it even surpassed all horoscopes, indeed all the prophets and their prophecies put together. Finally she complained to me of her troubles and desired to hear whether I knew a way to charm her fickle lover and to bring him back to her door.

"But, of course, noble lady!" I said, "He cannot but return and become your obedient servant once more, and even if he should bear armor like the great Goliath himself." Nothing could have been more pleasing to the ears of this enamored ninny, and she desired nothing but that my art be immediately set to work. I said we must be alone and everything must be done with the greatest discretion. Thereupon her maids were dismissed and charged to keep silent; I, however, went with the *mademoiselle* to her bedroom. I requested of her the mourning veil which she had used when mourning for her father, *item* two earrings, a valuable necklace which she happened to be wearing, her belt, and her favorite ring. When I had these jewels I wrapped them up in the veil, made several knots in it, murmured various nonsensical words, and put all of it in the lovelorn lady's bed; after this I said: "We must go to the cellar together." When we arrived there I persuaded her to undress down to her shift, and while this was being done, I wrote some mysterious characters on the butt of a large wine barrel, then drew out the tap, and ordered the lady to stop the hole with her finger till I had executed the same art with the tap upstairs in the house as with the other things. Now when I had thus tied up the foolish thing, as it were, I went and fetched the jewels from her bed and without delay left the town with them.

But either this pious, gullible, lovestricken fool and her possessions were protected by a merciful heaven or her jewels were somehow else not meant for me; for before I had even reached our camp with my booty, a highborn officer from the garrison caught me and demanded them of me. I denied everything, of course, but he proved me wrong. I cannot say that he cudgeled me, but I can swear that he flatsworded me right smartly. For when he had his servant dismount to search me and I, to prevent it, met the latter with my terrible gypsy knife, look you, he whipped out his sword and not only covered my head with lumps but beat me so black and blue on the arms, hips, and shoulders that for a whole month I was obliged to rub salves on them to get rid of the bruises. And I truly believe that devil would be beating me still this very hour if I had not thrown down my booty. And this was my reward this time, both for my pretty inventiveness and the artful fraud itself.

Chapter 28

Courage comes with her company into a village where a church festival is being held, and incites a young gypsy to shoot a hen; her husband pretends he intends to hang him; when everyone ran out of the village to watch this spectacle the gypsy women stole everything roasted and baked and quickly and cunningly escaped with their whole band

Not long after this unfortunate battle, our gypsy band left the Königsmark troops and went back to the Swedish main army, which Torstenson[1] was at that time commanding and leading into Bohemia, where both armies then joined.[2] I and my mule remained with this armada not only till after the peace treaty was signed, but also did not leave the gypsies either even after peace had already been declared, because I did not feel confident that I could rid myself of the habit of stealing. And since I see that my scribe still has one white sheet of paper left, I will, for a finish or *valete*, tell and have him set down a little trick which I thought up only recently and which was immediately tried and tested, from which the Reader may guess what else I may have accomplished and how well I fit in with the gypsies.

Once, in the Lorraine territory, we came towards eventide to a large village where they were just celebrating a church festival, for which reason and because we had a pretty large troop of men, women, children, and horses, we were refused shelter for the night. But my husband, who passed himself off as a lieutenant colonel,[3] promised on

1. *Torstenson*] Lennart, Count von Ortala (1603–1651), took over command of the Swedish army in 1641.
2. *joined*] in September and October of 1646.
3. *lieutenant colonel*] only through the fraudulent behavior of her gypsy man does Courage finally attain to a rank higher than captain.

his "honor as a nobleman" that he would make good all damages and
that he himself would pay for anything which was spoilt or stolen and
in addition would punish the evildoer at the cost of life and limb, with
which assurances he finally after much effort gained permission for us
to camp there. Everywhere in the village there was the smell of roasting and baking, so delicious that I straightway felt the desire for this
food and was vexed that the peasants should eat it all alone by themselves and therefore straightway invented a ruse by which we could get
hold of it ourselves.

I had an alert young fellow from our band shoot a hen in front of
the inn, whereupon a complaint against the wrongdoer was soon
lodged with my husband. My husband acted terribly angry and
straightway had the man with us who acted as trumpeter call our band
together. Now when this had happened and both peasants and gypsies
were together in the marketplace, I told several of our people in our
thieves' language about my plan and that every woman should be
ready for pilfering. So my husband held a short trial for the wrongdoer
and sentenced him to death by the rope, because he had disobeyed his
lieutenant colonel's command. Thereupon there was straightway a
great clamor in the village that the lieutenant colonel was going to
have a gypsy hanged just for the sake of a hen. Some thought this
procedure too rigorous, others praised us for keeping such good order.
One of our men was obliged to act as executioner, which person
immediately tied the malefactor's hands behind his back; however, a
young gypsy woman pretended to be his wife, borrowed three children
from another, and came running to the square with them. She begged
them to spare her husband's life and to think of their little children,
acting as pitiable as if she were about to despair; but my husband
would neither see nor hear her, but instead had the evildoer led out to
the woods in order to have the sentence carried out, just at the point
when he guessed the whole village was assembled to see the poor
sinner hang, and indeed almost all the inhabitants, young and old,
man and wife, manservant and maidservant, kith and kin, went out

Au bout du comté ils trennent pour droit
Qu'ils sont venus d'Aegipte a ce Feste

14. Gypsies Preparing a Feast. From *The Gypsies*. 1621

with us for this purpose. But the above-mentioned young gypsy woman with her three borrowed children did not forbear to howl, scream and plead; and when they all came to the woods and to a certain tree upon which, to all appearances, the chicken-murderer was to be hanged, she acted so miserable that first the peasant women and finally the peasants themselves began to intervene for the misdoer and did not stop till my husband let them persuade him to spare the poor sinner's life on her account.

Now while we were thus playing this comedy outside the village, our women inside the village stole everything at will; because they had not only emptied the roasting spits and bake-ovens but had also fished quite a bit of plunder out of the wagons here and there; they left the village and came to meet us, acting as if they were egging their husbands on to rebel against me and my husband for wishing to hang a brave man on account of a scrawny chicken, thereby making his poor wife a widow and his three innocent young children orphans. But in our own language they told us that they had snatched good booty, with which it was high time we shook the dust from our heels, before the peasants became aware of their loss. Thereupon I shouted to our people to act rebellious and to take flight into the woods. These my husband and those still with him pursued with drawn swords, indeed they even fired off several shots, as did the others, but with no intention at all of hitting anyone. The peasant folk were affrighted by the impending blood bath and therefore wished to return home quickly; but we chased one another, constantly shooting, deep into the woods, where our people knew every path and trail. *In summa*, we marched all night and in the morning not only divided up our booty but separated into smaller bands, by which stratagem we, with our booty, escaped the peasants and all other dangers.

With these people I have since visited every corner of *Europae* several times and invented, devised, and carried out very many rascally and thievish tricks, so that one would need a whole ream of paper if one wished to tell all of them. Indeed, I do not think a ream would be enough; and just for this reason nothing has astonished me more in my whole life than that they suffer us in any country, since we desire neither to be of use nor to serve either God or man, but nourish ourselves by lying, cheating, and stealing, to the detriment of the peasant as well as the great lords themselves, whose game we eat. But of this I must keep silent so that I may cause no trouble for us, and anyway, I think I have revealed sufficiently, to the eternal shame of Simplicissimo, what breed of cat he shared a bed with in Sauerbrunnen and so magnificently bragged about to the whole world; indeed, I believe too that more than once when he thought he was enjoying a beautiful lady, he was being deceived by French whores like me and probably even by broomstick-riders, thereby even becoming the devil's own kinsman.

Addendum of the Author[1]

Now, for this reason then, you chaste youths, you honorable widowers, and even you married men who have hitherto avoided these dangerous *chimeris*, eluded these terrible medusas, stopped your ears against these cursed sirens and forsworn these unfathomable and bottomless *belidibus*,[2] or at least withstood them by fleeing, let these *Lupas*[3] not henceforth enchant you in the future; for one thing is certain: That there is nought else to be expected from loving whores than all manner of uncleanness, shame, ridicule, poverty, and misery, and worst of all a bad conscience too. Only when it is too late does one realize what one had in them, how nasty they are, how vile, how lice-ridden, scabby, unclean, stinking both of breath and of their whole body, how full of French disease within and full of pustulent sores without; so that in the end one must, in his own heart, be ashamed of it and, ofttimes, much too late, deplore it.

1. The whole is borrowed from Garzonis, *Allgemeiner Schauplatz* (Frankfurt, 1599), p. 838.
2. *belidibus*] (dative) the granddaughters of Belos, the fifty daughters of Danaos, who killed their husbands on their wedding night.
3. *Lupas* (accusative) female wolves.

Appendix A

The full titles of the first editions of *Simplicissimus* and of the three Simplician novels are:

Der Abentheurliche Simplicissimus Teutsch. Das ist: Die Beschreibung desz Lebens eines seltzamen Vaganten, genant Melchior Sternfels von Fuchshaim, wo und welcher gestalt Er nemlich in diese Welt kommen, was er darinn gesehen, gelernet, erfahren und auszgestanden, auch warumb er solche wieder freywillig quittirt. Überausz lustig, und manniglich nützlich zu lesen. An Tag geben von German Schleifheim von Sulsfort. Mompelgart, Gedruckt bey Johann Fillion, Im Jahr MDCLXIX.

Trutz Simplex: Oder Ausführliche und wunderseltzame Lebensbeschreibung Der Ertzbetrügerin und Landstörtzerin Courasche, Wie sie anfangs eine Rittmeisterin, hernach eine Hauptmännin, ferner eine Leutnantin, bald eine Marcketenterin, Muszquetirerin, und letzlich eine Ziegeunerin abgegeben, Meisterlich agiret, und ausbündig vorgestellet: Eben so lustig, annemlich un nützlich zu betrachten, als Simplicissimi selbst. Alles miteinander Von der Courasche eigner Person dem weit und breitbekanten Simplicissimo zum Verdrusz und Widerwillen, dem Autori in die Feder dictirt, der sich vor diszmal nennet Philarchus Grossus von Trommenheim, aufs Griffsberg, etc. Gedruckt in Utopia, bey Felix Stratiot.

Der seltzame Springinsfeld, das ist Kurtzweilige, lusterweckende und recht lächerliche Lebens-Beschreibung Eines weiland frischen, wolversuchten und tapffern Soldaten, Nunmehro aber ausgemergelten, abgelebten doch dabey recht verschlagnen Landstörtzers und Bettlers, Samt seiner wunderlichen Gauckeltasche. Aus Anordnung des weit und breitbekanten Simplicissimi Verfasset und zu Papier gebracht Von Philarcho Grosso von Tromenheim. Gedruckt in Paphlagonia bey Felix Stratiot. Anno 1670.

Das wunderbarliche Vogelnest der Springinsfeldischen Leirerin, voller abenteurlicher, doch lehrreicher Geschichten, auf simplicianische Art sehr nützlich und kurzweilig zu lesen ausgefertigt durch Michael Rechulin von Sehmsdorff. Mompelgart, gedruckt bei Johann Fillion, im zuendlaufenden 1672. Jahr.

Des wunderbarlichen Vogelnests zweiter Teil. An Tag geben von Aceeeffghhiillmmnnoorrssstuu (Anagramm für Grimmelshausen).

The titles of the other Simplician writings are:

Simplicianischer Zwyköpffiger Ratio Status . . . von Hans Jacob Christoph Von Grimmelshausen, Gelnhusano, Nürnberg, Gedruckt und zu finden bey Wolf Eberhard Felszeckern, im Jahr Christi 1670.

Des Abenteuerlichen Simplicii Verkehrte Welt . . . entworffen von Simon Lengfrisch von Hartenfels, Gedruckt im Jahr 1672.

Rathstübel Plutonis Oder Kunst reich zu werden . . . von Erich Steinfels von Grufensholm . . . Getruckt in Samarien. Im Jahr 1672.

Simplicissimi Galgen-Männlin, Oder ausführlicher Bericht woher man die sogenannten Allraungen oder Geldmännlein bekommt . . . Nachgehends mit nützlichen Anmerk- und Erinnerungen erläutert durch Israel Fromschmidt von Hugenfelsz.

The titles of the two courtly novels included in the collected works are:

Dietwalts und Amelinden anmuthige Liebs- und Leidsbeschreibung, Sammt erster Vergrösserung des Weltberühmten Königreichs Franckreich. Den Gottseeligen erbaulich, Curiosen lustig, Historicis annemlich, Betrübten tröstlich, Verliebten erfreulich, Politicis nützlich und der Jugend ohnärgerlich zu lesen. Zusammengesucht und hervorgehoben von H. J. Christoffel von Grimmelshausen, Gelnhusano. Nürnberg, Verlegt und zu finden bey Felszeckern, Im Jahr Christi 1670.

Des durchleuchtigen Printzen Proximi, und Seiner ohnvergleichlichen Lympidae Liebs-Geschicht-Erzehlung . . . von H. J. Christoffel von Grimmelshausen, Gelnhusano.

Appendix B

As indicated in the introduction, both *The Runagate Courage* and *The Strange Hopalong* are continuations of *Simplicissimus*. Given here are the chapters in *Hopalong* which concern Courage. The situation is as follows: the narrator, a young student, meets two strangers at an inn: an aged man of imposing appearance whom he recognizes as the world-famous Simplicissimus, or Simplicius, and a hardbitten, foul-mouthed, evil-tempered old soldier. This is Hopalong, Simplicius' comrade-in-arms and Courage's former lover, now a one-legged veteran reduced to earning his living as a wandering fiddler. The student tells the two men how he met Courage, how he was employed to write her autobiography, and how she paid him off. It should be noted that in the German original (and, hopefully, in this rendering) the style differs somewhat from that used in *The Runagate Courage*. The narrator tends to a sort of naive pomposity which seems to be alien to Courage's character.

From Chapter 4

. . . Then I turned to Hopalong and asked him whether he had not had in Italy a concubine by the name of Courage. He answered: "That bloody witch! May lightning strike her dead! Is that devil still alive? Since God created the world the sun has never shone on a more wanton *bestia*."

"Now, now," Simplicius said to him, "what manner of wanton heedless talk is this?"

But to me he said: "Pray continue, or rather begin the tale which I so heartily desire to hear."

I answered: "Noble sir, you will probably soon tire of it, for she is that same woman whom you yourself mentioned in the sixth chapter of the fifth book of your life history."

"No matter," answered Simplicius, "just tell what you know of her, and do not spare my feelings either." Thereupon I told what Simplicius desired to know, in the following manner.

At the very end of last autumn, when, as everyone knows, there was a delightful Indian summer, I was on my way from my fatherland to the Rhine, to the place where we are now, in fact, where I hoped either to continue my studies while working as a tutor, as is customary with poor students, or to find a post as a clerk, which had been recommended to me by my relatives, from whom I had received letters of introduction for this purpose; now as I was wandering along the crest of the Black Forest on this side of Krummenschiltach, I saw in the distance a sizable group of ragtag rabble coming towards me whom I at first glance recognized to be gypsies, and I was not mistaken either; and because I did not trust them I hid in the thickest part of a hedge; but these fellows had with them many dogs, both trackers and greyhounds, and they straightway caught my scent, surrounded me, and began to bark as if they had found a piece of game; their masters heard this and hastened up with their guns or long bandoleer muskets to where I was; one posted himself here, another there, just like hunters watching for flushed and driven game. Now when I saw with my own eyes what danger I was in, particularly since the dogs were already beginning to snap at me, I began to cry out as if they had already put the hunting knife to my throat; thereupon everyone—men, women, boys, and girls—ran up, and there was so much ado that I could not tell whether these nasty people meant to kill me or to save me from their dogs. Indeed, in my fright I imagined that they murdered people like me whom they caught in lonely places and afterwards even ate them up so that their murder might go undetected. I wondered too, and I still do, why such infamous gangs of thieves are permitted to rove about the land with their dogs and guns, and I cursed those responsible for the game and hunting rights for tolerating them.

Now when I found myself surrounded by them this way, like a poor wretch who is about to be hanged and who himself doesn't know whether he be still alive or already half dead, look you, there came riding up on a mule a magnificent gypsy woman, the likes of whom I had never seen or heard of in all my days, for which reason I could not but take her to be at least a distinguished princess, over all the other gypsy women, if not the queen of the gypsies herself! She appeared to be a person of about sixty years, but as I have since reckoned she was one or six years older than that; she did not even have pitch-black hair like the others, but rather it was somewhat yellowish and gathered together with a string of gold and precious stones like a crown, not with a simple band like other gypsy women wear, or with a piece of gauze or a veil or even with just a withe; one could see by her face, which was still smooth, that in her youth she had not been ugly; in her ears she wore earrings fashioned in gold and enamel and studded with diamonds, and around her neck was a string of matched pearls of which a princess need not have been ashamed; her cape was not of rough blanket cloth but of scarlet and was lined with green velvet; both her cape and her skirt, which was of expensive green English cloth, were trimmed with silver lace; she wore neither bodice nor doublet, but did have on a pair of jolly Polish boots; the seams of her shirt were stitched in the Bohemian manner with black silk and it was of pure, snow-white Urach[1] linen, so that all in all she looked like a huckleberry in a bowl of milk; nor did she carry her long gypsy knife hidden under her skirt, but had it in the open, because it was so beautiful that it well deserved to be displayed; and if I am to confess the truth, it still seems to me that the old hag, especially on assback (I very nearly said on horseback), looked extremely good in this costume; and to this very day I can see her this way in my imagination whenever I wish.

Chapter 5

In which Courage dictates her life history to the author

Now this preposterous gypsy woman, whom the others all called Milady, but whom I should have taken to be the spitting image of the

1. *Urach*] in Württemberg, already had a textile industry.

Lady of Babylon [1] if she had only been astride a seven-headed dragon and had been a bit more beautiful, said to me: "Ah, my pretty young fair-skinned fellow, what are you doing here all alone and so far from other people?"

I answered: "Most noble and powerful lady, my home is in Switzerland, and it is my intention to journey to a city on the Rhine, either to continue my studies there or to go into service, for I am a poor student."

"Well, God keep you, my child," she said and then she asked, "Would you not like to serve me with your quill for a day or a fortnight and write something down for me? I would give you a dollar a day."

I thought: "A dollar a day is not to be spurned, but who knows what you will have to write? Such a grand offer must be considered suspect." And if she herself had not said that God should keep me, I should have thought that she was an apparition of the devil who wished to beguile me with this money and take me into that miserable congregation, the witches' covey. My answer was: "If it will do me no harm, Milady, I shall write whatever you desire."

"But of course not, my child," she replied, "it will not do you any harm at all, God forbid, now come along with us; I shall give you food and drink in the bargain, the best I have, till you have finished the work."

Now because I had no more food in my stomach than I had money in my purse, which was empty, and particularly since I was the prisoner of these thieves, look you, I went along with them, namely into a thick forest where we camped the first night and where several fellows were already at work butchering a handsome stag; now they began lighting fires, cooking and roasting; and as far as I could tell, and afterwards this was completely confirmed, Milady Libushka, for that was the name of my gypsy woman, was in command of every-

1. *Babylon*] "... and I saw a woman sit upon a scarlet colored beast, full of names of blasphemy, having seven heads and ten horns" (Rev. 17:3).

thing; a tent of white fustian, which she had under the saddle of her mule, was put up for her. She, however, led me off a little to one side, sat down under a tree, bade me to sit down beside her, and drew forth the life history of Simplicissimus.

"Look you, my friend," she said, "this knave, about whom this book is written, has played me the scurviest trick that was ever played me in all my living days, which so pains me that I find it impossible to let his knavery go unavenged; for after he had sufficiently enjoyed my gracious good will, this ungrateful rascal (noble sir, forgive me for using her own words) saw fit not only to forsake me and to rid himself of me by means of as wicked a trick as was ever heard of, but then even went and proclaimed to the whole world his everlasting disgrace and my own. To be sure, I have already paid him back properly for that first prank he played on me. My chambermaid had been left with an illegitimate child at the very time when this fine fellow was keeping company with me in Sauerbrunnen. When I heard that he had gotten married I had this child baptized in his name and left on his doorstep with a note that I myself had conceived and borne this fruit by him, which caused him to believe that he was obliged to accept and bring up this child as his own, to his own great dishonor; and on top of that he was severely punished by his magistrate; this deceit came off so well that I would not take a thousand sovereigns for it, particularly since I learned to my great joy only recently that this bastard is to be the sole heir of the deceived deceiver."

Simplicius, who had been listening attentively, interrupted me at this point and said: "If I still found pleasure in that sort of foolishness, as I once did, it would greatly amuse me to hear that this foolish woman imagines that she pulled the wool over my eyes in this matter, since actually she has done me the greatest service while to this day deceiving herself with vain dreams; for at the time when I was making up to her I lay more often with her chambermaid than with her herself; and it is much more agreeable to me that this same chambermaid and not that wanton gypsy woman is the mother of my son, Simplicius, whom I cannot disown since he takes after me in both mind and body. But here is an example of how those who think to deceive others often deceive themselves and of how God is wont to punish the great sins of those who will not reform with even greater sins, so that their final damnation is that much greater; but pray continue with your tale; what else did she say?"

I obeyed and continued in the following manner: She commanded me to acquaint myself a little with your biography, noble sir, so that I might use it as a model, for it was her desire that I write down her life story in this very same manner, in order to communicate it likewise to the whole wide world, for the sole purpose of spiting you, Simplicissimus, so that everyone should laugh at your folly; she said I should forget all other thoughts and cares which I might be entertaining at present so that I could attend the better to this work; in the meantime she would secure paper, ink and quill and would pay me, once the work was completed, so that I could not but be satisfied with her.

So for the first two days I had nothing else to do but to read, to gorge myself with food, and to sleep, during which time, noble sir, I finished up your life history; but on the third day when the writing was to begin, there was an unexpected alarm, not because anyone attacked or pursued us, but because a lone gypsy woman, disguised as a poor beggar, arrived in camp, bringing with her rich booty which she had snatched, such as silverware, rings, medallions, baptismal presents, and all sorts of things which are generally put around childrens' necks at christenings; at once there was a curious clamor and then a hasty departure; Courage (for that is what this most distinguished gypsy woman called herself in her *Spite-Simplex*) gave orders and divided the whole rabble into various troupes, instructing them which road each troupe was to take and also how, where, and when they should come together again at a certain place which she named. Now when in an instant the entire company had split up like quicksilver and disappeared, Courage herself, together with the ablest and best armed gypsy men and women, rode down into the Black Forest in such great haste as if she herself had stolen the things and were being pursued by a whole army; she did not stop running either till we had put many valleys behind us and had reached the large tall forests on the uppermost crest of the Black Forest above the Murg River;[2] there we again set up our camp; a horse had been assigned to me for this rapid journey, and on it I fared as the old saw says: Who seldom rides must suffer in his &c.

I well remarked that this retinue of Courage, which counting me consisted only of men and women and thirteen horses, but of no children, carried and safeguarded all of the gold, silver, and jewels that the other gypsies had stolen. Nothing astounded me more than the fact that these people knew so well all the paths, all the highways and byways in this wild, desolate region and that with this otherwise disorderly mob everything was so well arranged, and was done in a more orderly fashion than in many a household. Scarcely had we eaten that same evening and rested a little when two of the women were clad in the traditional dress of the region and sent to Horb[3] under the pretext of buying bread for a village innkeeper, while at the same time one of the men rode to Gernsbach[4] and brought back the next day a few barrels of wine which, so he told anyone who asked, he had bought from a vintner.

It was here, noble Sir, that this godless Courage began to dictate to me her *Spite-Simplex*, as she called it, or better, the story of her wanton life; she did not talk to me in gypsy dialect, but instead in a manner which showed her good intellect and also made it clear that she had lived with gentlefolk and through the wondrous vagaries of fortune had seen the world far and wide, learning and experiencing much. I found her extremely vengeful, and I cannot but believe that Anacharsis[5] himself must have been her teacher, and because of this

2. *Murg River*] Courage's flight takes her along the crest of the Black Forest from the south to the north, to Baden-Baden.

3. *Horb*] on the Neckar River.

4. *Gernsbach*] in the Murg Valley.

5. *Anacharsis*] Scythian prince regarded by the Greeks as an unspoiled child of nature; not known for his vengefulness.

godless inclination she had the aforementioned treatise written in her own name in order to honor you, Sir. I shall say no more as to the content of this same treatise, since no doubt she will have it printed soon.

Chapter 6

The Author continues with the aforementioned Materia *and tells of the thanks which he received from Courage as payment for his services as a clerk*

Simplicius asked how Hopalong had gotten involved with her and what she had had to do with him. I answered: "As far as I can still remember, she was his concubine in Italia as I have already mentioned, or rather, to all appearances, he was her servant, especially since (if what this slut told me be true) she also gave him the name of Hopalong."

"Quiet, you villain, a plague on you!" said Hopalong. "Quiet, you quill-driver, or by God, I'll lay this candlestick across your skull and see the color of your blood!" And to make good his words he snatched up the candlestick, but Simplicius was just as quick and far stronger than he and was also of a different mind, for which reason he prevented him from striking the blow and threatened to throw him out the window if he did not calm himself; in the meantime the innkeeper came in and ordered us to keep the peace, expressly threatening that if we were not quiet the bailiffs and turnkeys would soon appear to conduct the troublemaker, or perhaps even all three of us, to different lodgings. Now although I straightway began to tremble with fear when I heard this and became as quiet as a mouse, I still did not wish to suffer such insults, but intended to go to the mayor and lodge a complaint in regard to the injury which had been done me; but Simplicius and the innkeeper, who had seen Hopalong's ducats and hoped to lay hold of a few of them, consoled me most persuasively so that I changed my mind, although Hopalong kept on growling at me like a vicious old dog. Finally it was agreed that if Hopalong apologised to me I should forgive him for the way he had insulted me, and I should furthermore be the guest of Hopalong and Simplicissimi for as long as I liked.

After this agreement Simplicius asked me how I had gotten away from the so-called gypsies again and in what pursuits they had passed their time in the forest. I answered: "In eating, drinking, sleeping, dancing, fornicating, smoking, singing, wrestling, fencing, and jumping about. The main work of the women was cooking and making fires, except for a few old crones who sat about and instructed the young girls in how to tell fortunes, or rather, how to lie. Some of the men hunted game, without doubt casting a magic spell over it so that it must needs stand still, and it was their practice to kill the game by using spent powder which made no sound when fired off, and I certainly remarked among them no lack of either wild game or domestic animals. We had hardly been camped there two days when again one party after the other began to arrive, among them some whom I had hitherto not yet seen; some (who were of course not kindly received) asked to borrow money from Courage (I guess from the common hoard), but others brought in booty, and none appeared without bringing along either bread, butter, bacon, chickens, geese, ducks, suckling pigs, goats, mutton, or even well-fatted swine, except for one poor old crone who arrived without any booty but a backside beaten black and blue, as she had been caught in a criminal act and rewarded for her pains with ringing cuffs and blows; and I suppose, as is easy to imagine, that they either stole the above-mentioned domestic animals or else cut them out of some herd or other; while such companies arrived in our camp daily, some of us also left camp every day, to be sure not always as gypsies, but rather dressed in the manner, I suppose, which was suitable for whatever thievish tricks they had planned; and these, noble sir, were the pursuits of the gypsies which I observed for as long as I was with them.

Now, noble sir, since you demand it, I shall tell you how I got away from them again, although my acquaintanceship with Courage does me as little honor as Hopalong's did him or even yours did you, Simplice.

I was not able to write for more than three or four hours a day, because Courage took no more time than that to dictate to me; and when I was through for the day I was permitted to take walks, play, and amuse myself with the others, whereby all and sundry showed themselves amenable and well-disposed toward me; indeed, Courage herself kept me company most of the time, because these people have in their lives no place at all for any sadness, sorrow, or grief; they reminded me of weasels and foxes, the way they lived in freedom and spent their days stealing, cautious and sly and ready to shake the dust from their heels in an instant whenever they remarked themselves to be in danger. Once Courage asked me how I liked this life of freedom, and I answered: "Very much!"; and though everything I said was a lie, I even added that I had wished more than once that I could be a gypsy too.

"My son," said she, "if you have a hankering to stay with us, it can be arranged."

"Yes, milady," I answered, "if only I could speak the language!"

"You will soon learn it," said she, "I learned it myself in less than six months. If you stay with us, I shall get you a pretty girl to sleep with."

I answered that I wished to think it over for a few more days and decide whether I might expect to find a better life any place else; I claimed I had long since tired of studying and sitting over my books night and day, and I did not wish to work either, much less learn a trade; and to top it all I could expect but a niggling *patrimonium* from my parents.

"You show great wisdom, my son," the old crowbait went on, "and you can see and discern how much better our way of life is, namely when you consider that not a one of our children would let even the greatest prince take him away and adopt him and make a gentleman of him. Our children count such high princely favors for naught, while other slavish people greatly desire them."

I let her think she had won me over, but in my mind I felt about her the same way Hopalong did, for by pretending that I wished to stay with her I hoped to receive permission that much sooner to leave camp with the others and thereby find an opportunity to escape.

At just this time a band of gypsies arrived, bringing with them a young gypsy maiden who was more beautiful than even the most beautiful of these people generally are; she, as well as other maids, soon became acquainted with me (for you must know that unmarried gypsies, because of their sloth, do not shy away from love-making, nor are they ashamed of it), and she proved to be so friendly, charming, and winning that I believe I should have come to an agreement with her if I had not feared that I should be obliged to learn witchcraft and if I had not but recently heard of Courage's wanton and wicked life from her own lips; for just this reason I was that much more cautious and careful, but I acted more agreeable toward her than toward any other of the gypsy women. Straightway after we had become acquainted she asked me what I was writing down for the "countess," for that is what she called Courage. But when I answered that she had no need to know that, she was quite satisfied with this reply, and I thought I remarked too from the way Courage behaved that she herself had bade the girl ask me this question, to test my discretion, for, or at least so I foolishly thought, she became more and more friendly to me.

By then I had already gone two weeks without ever once taking off my clothes, for which reason I began to be plagued by lice, which secret suffering I confided to my gypsy lass; at first she laughed mightily at my plight and called me a simple-minded booby; but the next morning she brought me a salve which was supposed to drive all lice away if I would sit naked by the fire, as is the custom of the gypsies, and let someone smear me all over with it, which task the lass herself was willing to perform. But I was much too ashamed to let her do it, and besides, I feared that the same thing might happen to me that had happened to Apulejo,[1] whom a similar treatment had transformed into

1. *Apulejo*] Apuleius, author of *The Golden Ass*, a late Roman novel.

an ass. But in time the varmint began to torture me so much that I could no longer bear it, for which reason I was forced to make use of this salve treatment, but with the proviso that I would not hold still and let her treat me till I had first greased her all over; to this purpose we made a fire some distance away from our camp and there did as we had agreed to.

The lice were driven away all right, but the next morning my skin and hair was so black that I looked like the devil himself; I did not know this myself till Courage began to tease me, saying: "Well, my son, I see that you have already given in to your desire and have become a real gypsy."

"Not that I know of, honored mother," I answered. But she said: "Look at your hands," and with that she had them bring me a mirror, and she pointed to a figure in it which I did not recognize as my own and which frightened me, for it was exceeding black in color.

"This salving, my child," she said, "means as much to us as circumcision does to the Turks, and the girl who salved you must henceforth be your wife, whether you like her or not." And with that this Satan's brood began to laugh as if they were about to burst.

Now when I saw how matters stood I felt like cursing heaven and hell; but what could I do but accommodate myself to the will of those who at that time had me in their power? "Ha!" I said. "What do I care? Do you think perhaps that this change grieves me? Stop laughing and tell me instead when my wedding will be."

"Whenever you wish," Courage answered. "Whenever you wish, but let us wait till we can have a priest present too."

At that time I was already finished with Courage's life history, except that I was supposed to add a few thievish capers, I know not of what sort, which she had perpetrated since she had become a gypsy; therefore I very politely requested the wages I had been promised; but she said: "Oh, my son, you need no money now; it will come in handy after you have married." I thought: "The devil must have given you the idea that you could hold me here this way." And when she remarked that I was looking somewhat sour she named and appointed me the highest *secretarium* for the Egyptian Nation and promised me that my wedding with her young cousin should take place at the earliest opportunity and that I should receive as dowry two beautiful horses; and so that I might be that much more convinced that this was so, my bride was enjoined to entertain me with her customary amiability.

Shortly after all this had happened we broke camp, and about thirty of us, including women and children, marched slowly and in good order down the Buehl Valley; for this journey Courage did not wear her splendid costume but rather was dressed like any other old witch; I was with the foragers and helped raid several farms, during which duty I may say that I was no slouch but indeed a leader among the foremost of the gypsies. The next day we marched all the way to the Rhine and spent the night in a thicket near a village where there was a ferry on which we were to cross the Rhine the next day. But in the morning, when the black-skinned *secretarius* awoke, look you, the poor fellow found himself quite alone, for all the gypsies, including his bride, had deserted him completely, so that he had nothing to remember them by except his charming color.

Chapter 7

Now there I sat as if God himself had forsaken me, though I had good reason to be grateful to Him that this wanton rabble had not murdered me or stripped me in my sleep and stolen what little money I still carried with me for food. And you, Hopalong, what reason have you now to rage at me, since I am voluntarily relating how I was cheated, as were you, by this vicious slut whose cunning and malice are such that no man can escape them once she has fixed upon him, as was very nearly the case with our honorable Simplicissimo?

"None," answered Hopalong. "None whatsoever, good friend. Let us forget it, and the devil take that witch!"

"Pray," Simplicius answered him, "Don't wish the poor ninny any worse ill yet; have you not heard that she is close to damnation as it is, up to her ears in the mire of wickedness and sin, if not already in the jaws of hell? Rather say a few reverent Paternosters for her sake, that the kindness of God may illuminate her heart and bring her to true repentance!"

"What," said Hopalong, "I'd rather lightning strike her dead."

"Oh, God save us," answered Simplicius, "I assure you that if you persist in this I should not wish to have to say which one of you two will find eternal salvation."

To this Hopalong replied, "What do I care?" But good Simplicius shook his head with a deep sigh. . . .